Standard

AIRCRAFT
HANDBOOK

5TH EDITION

AIRCRAFT
HANDBOOK

5TH EDITION

EDITED BY LARRY REITHMAIER,
ORIGINALLY COMPILED AND EDITED BY
STUART LEAVELL AND STANLEY BUNGAY

Distributed by:
Airlife Publishing Ltd.
101 Longden Road, Shrewsbury SY3 9EB, England

FIFTH EDITION
FOURTH PRINTING

© 1991 by **TAB/AERO Books**, an imprint of TAB Books.
TAB Books is a division of McGraw-Hill, Inc.
Earlier editions copyright 1952, 1958, 1980, and 1986 by TAB Books.

Library of Congress Cataloging-in-Publication Data

Standard aircraft handbook.—5th ed. / edited by Larry Reithmaier ;
  originally compiled and edited by Stuart Leavell and Stanley Bungay.
      p.   cm.
   Includes index.
   ISBN 0-8306-8634-7
   1. Airplanes—Design and construction. I. Reithmaier, L. W.
(Lawrence W.), 1921- . II. Leavell, Stuart. III. Bungay,
Stanley.
TL671.28.S69   1991
629.134'2—dc20   90-28495
                                                  CIP

Acquisitions Editor: Jeff Worsinger
Book Editor: Norval Kennedy
Director of Production: Katherine G. Brown   AS1

Contents

Acknowledgments

Extensive use was made of data, information, illustrations and photographs supplied by:

Lockheed Corporation
Rockwell International, NAAO
Federal Aviation Administration
Hi-Shear Corporation
Snap-On Tools
L.S. Starrett
The Aluminum Association
U.S. Industrial Tool & Supply
Lufkin Rule
Townsend Textron (Boots, Cherry fasteners)
Aeroquip
Parts suppliers catalogs.

Introduction

In keeping with the policy of maintaining the *Standard Aircraft Handbook* up-to-date, this fifth edition has been prepared. Like the fourth edition, all chapters have been revised to some extent. Also, the chapter sequence has been revised to present a more logical order. For example, the chapter on tools and their use, which includes safety considerations, is now chapter 1.

Drills and drilling have been removed from the chapter on tools and their proper use to become a separate chapter.

The chapter on materials and fabricating was revised to eliminate the detailed discussion of heat treatment because this requires special techniques and equipment that are usually associated with manufacturers or large repair stations.

Drilling and countersinking is now a separate chapter and somewhat expanded with new illustrations.

The chapter on riveting was somewhat revised to improve clarity with new illustrations.

The former chapter on assembly and installation methods became two separate chapters: Aircraft Plumbing, and Control Cables.

The standard parts chapter was completely revised to replace the original hardware drawings with new illustrations and titles containing more complete information.

Additional data was included in the appendix.

The *Standard Aircraft Handbook* is presented in shop terms for the aviation mechanic engaged in building, maintaining, overhauling, or repairing all-metal aircraft. It is also an excellent guide for the student mechanic.

The procedures and practices covered in this handbook are general and applicable to any aircraft. It is not intended, however, to replace the manufacturer's instructions, specifications, and approved practice, FAA, or other government regulations.

It is assumed that readers of this handbook already have a general knowledge of aircraft and their construction.

1

Tools and Their Proper Use

SAFETY CONSIDERATIONS

Before commencing work on an aircraft, one's personal safety must become habit. Putting on safety glasses must be as much a part of the act of drilling a hole as picking up the drill motor.

The responsibility for this attitude lies with the mechanic, but this responsibility goes further than that. A mechanic's family needs him whole, with both eyes intact, both hands with all fingers intact, and above all, in good health.

Safety glasses or face shields must be worn during all of the following operations:

- Drilling
- Reaming
- Countersinking
- Driving rivets
- Bucking rivets
- Operating rivet squeezer
- Operating any power tool
- Near flying chips or around moving machinery

Ear plugs should be used as protection against the harsh noises of the rivet gun and general factory din. If higher noise levels than the rivet gun are experienced, a full ear coverage *earmuff* should be used because it is a highly sound absorbent device.

For people who wear long hair, a snood-type cap that keeps the hair from entangling with turning drills should be worn. Shirt sleeves should be short, or long sleeves rolled up at least to the elbow. Closed-toe, low-heel shoes should be worn. Open-toed shoes, sandals, ballet slippers, moccasins, and canvas-

type shoes offer little or no protection for the foot and should not be worn in the shop or factory. Safety shoes are recommended.

Compressed air should not be used for cleaning clothes or equipment.

GENERAL-PURPOSE HAND TOOLS
Hammers

Hammers include *ball-peen* and *soft* hammers (Fig. 1-1). The ball-peen hammer is used with a punch, with a chisel, or as a peening (bending, indenting, or cutting) tool. Where there is danger of scratching or marring the work, a soft hammer (for example, brass, plastic, or rubber) is used. Most accidents with hammers occur when the hammerhead loosens. The hammer handle must fit the head tightly. A sweaty palm or an oily or greasy handle might let the hammer slip. Oil or grease on the hammer face might cause the head to slip off the work and cause a painful bruise. Striking a hardened steel surface sharply with a ball-peen hammer is a safety hazard. Small pieces of sharp, hardened steel might break from the hammer and also break from the hardened steel. The result might be an eye injury or damage to the work or the hammer. An appropriate soft hammer should be used to strike hardened steel. If the soft hammer is not available, a piece of copper, brass, fiber, or wood material should be placed on the hardened steel and struck with the hammer, not the hardened steel.

Fig. 1-1. Ball-peen and soft-face hammers.

Screwdrivers

The screwdriver is a tool for driving or removing screws. Screwdrivers frequently used are the *common*, *crosspoint*, and *offset*. Also in use are various screwdriver bits that are designed to fit screws having special heads. These special screwdrivers are discussed in chapter 5.

A common screwdriver must fill at least 75 percent of the screw slot (Fig. 1-2). If the screwdriver is the wrong size, it cuts and burrs the screw slot, making it worthless. A screwdriver with the wrong size blade might slip and damage adjacent parts of the structures. The common screwdriver is used only where slotted head screws or fasteners are found on aircraft.

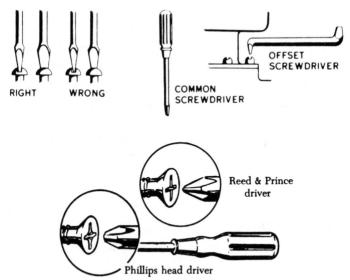

Fig. 1-2. Screwdrivers and their uses.

The two recessed head screws in common use are the *Phillips* and the *Reed and Prince*. As shown in Fig. 1-2, the Reed and Prince recessed head forms a perfect cross. The screwdriver used with this screw is pointed on the end. Because the Phillips screw has a slightly larger center in the cross, the Phillips screwdriver is blunt on the end. The Phillips screwdriver is not interchangeable with the Reed and Prince. The use of the wrong type screwdriver results in mutilation of the screwdriver and the screwhead.

A screwdriver should not be used for chiseling or prying.

Pliers

The most frequently used pliers in aircraft repair work include the *slip-joint*, *longnose*, *diagonal-cutting*, *water-pump*, and *vise-grip* types as shown in Fig. 1-3. The size of pliers indicates their overall length, usually ranging from 5 to 12 inches.

The 6-inch, slip-joint plier is the preferred size for use in repair work.

Slip-joint pliers are used to grip flat or round stock and to bend small pieces of metal to desired shapes. Longnose pliers are used to reach where the fingers alone cannot and to bend small pieces of metal. Diagonal-cutting pliers or *diagonals* or *dikes* are used to perform work such as cutting safety wire and removing cotter pins. Water-pump pliers, which have extra long handles, are used to

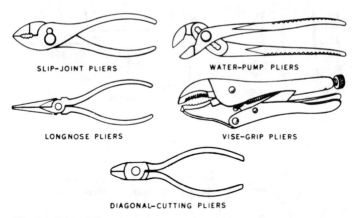

Fig. 1-3. Types of pliers.

obtain a very powerful grip. Vise-grip pliers (sometimes referred to as a *vise-grip wrench*) have many uses. Examples are to hold small work as a portable vise, to remove broken studs, and to pull cotter pins.

Pliers are not an all purpose tool. They are not to be used as a wrench for tightening a nut, for example. Tightening a nut with pliers causes damage to both the nut and the plier jaw serrations. Also, pliers should not be used as a prybar or as a hammer.

Punches

Punches are used to start holes for drilling, to punch holes in sheet metal, to remove damaged rivets, pins or bolts, and for aligning two or more parts for bolting together. A punch that has a mushroomed head should never be used. Flying pieces might cause an injury. Typical punches used by the aircraft mechanic are shown in Fig. 1-4.

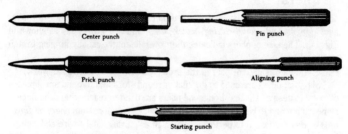

Fig. 1-4. Typical punches.

Wrenches

Wrenches are tools for tightening or removing nuts and bolts. The wrenches that are most often used are shown in Fig. 1-5: *open-end*, *box-end*, *adjustable*, *socket*, and *Allen* wrenches. All have special advantages. The good mechanic will choose the one best suited for the job at hand. Sockets are used with the various handles (*ratchet*, *hinge*, and *speed*) and *extension bars* shown in Fig. 1-5. Extension bars come in various lengths. The ratchet handle and speed wrench can be used in conjunction with suitable adapters and various type screwdriver bits to quickly install or remove special-type screws. However, if screws must be torqued to a specific torque value, a torque wrench must be used. Adjustable type wrenches should be used only when other wrenches do not fit. To prevent rounding off the corners of a nut, properly adjust the wrench. The wrench should always be pulled so that the handle moves toward the adjustable jaw. A wrench should always be pulled. It is dangerous to push on it. A pipe should not be used to increase wrench leverage. Doing so might break the wrench. A wrench should never be used as a hammer.

Proper torquing of nuts and bolts is important. Overtorquing or undertorquing might set up a hazardous condition. Specified torque values and procedures should always be observed.

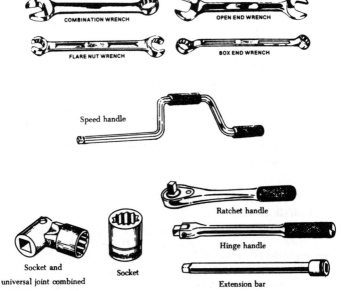

COMBINATION WRENCH

OPEN END WRENCH

FLARE NUT WRENCH

BOX END WRENCH

Speed handle

Ratchet handle

Hinge handle

Socket and
universal joint combined

Socket

Extension bar

Fig. 1-5. Wrenches and sockets.

Torque Wrenches

The three most commonly used torque wrenches are the *flexible beam*, *rigid frame*, and the *ratchet* types (Fig. 1-6). When using the flexible beam and the rigid frame torque wrenches, the torque value is read visually on a dial or scale mounted on the handle of the wrench.

To assure getting the correct amount of torque on the fasteners, all torque wrenches must be tested at least once a month or more often if necessary.

The standard torque table presented in chapter 5 should be used as a guide in tightening nuts, studs, bolts, and screws whenever specific torque values are not called out in maintenance procedures.

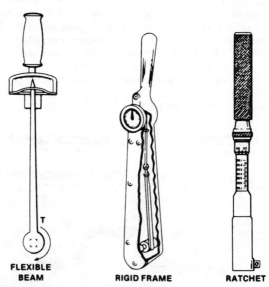

FLEXIBLE BEAM   RIGID FRAME   RATCHET

Fig. 1-6. Three common types of torque wrenches.

METAL CUTTING TOOLS
Hand Snips

Several hand snips serve a different purpose. *Straight, curved, hawksbill,* and *aviation* snips are in common use (Fig. 1-7). Straight snips are used for cutting straight lines when the distance is not great enough to use a squaring shear, and for cutting the outside of a curve. The other types are used for cutting the inside of curves or radii. Snips should never be used to cut heavy sheet metal.

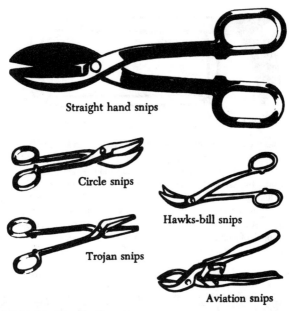

Fig. 1-7. Various types of snips.

Aviation snips are designed especially for cutting heat-treated aluminum alloy and stainless steel. They are also adaptable for enlarging small holes. The blades have small teeth on the cutting edges and are shaped for cutting very small circles and irregular outlines. The handles are the compound leverage type, making it possible to cut material as thick as 0.051 inch. Aviation snips are available in two types, those that cut from right to left and those that cut from left to right.

Unlike the hacksaw, snips do not remove any material when the cut is made, but minute fractures often occur along the cut. Therefore, cuts should be made about $1/32$ inch from the layout line and finished by hand-filing down to the line.

Hacksaws

The common hacksaw has a *blade*, a *frame*, and a *handle*. The handle can be obtained in two styles: *pistol grip* and *straight*. A pistol grip hacksaw is shown in Fig. 1-8.

When installing a blade in a hacksaw frame, the blade should be mounted with the teeth pointing forward, away from the handle.

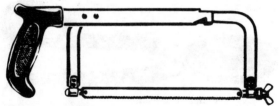

Fig. 1-8. Pistol grip hacksaw.

Blades are made of high-grade tool steel or tungsten steel and are available in sizes from 6 to 16 inches in length. The 10-inch blade is most commonly used. There are two types, the *all-hard* blade and the *flexible* blade. In flexible blades, only the teeth are hardened. Selection of the best blade for the job involves finding the right type of pitch. An all-hard blade is best for sawing brass, tool steel, cast iron, and heavy cross-section materials. A flexible blade is usually best for sawing hollow shapes and metals having a thin cross section.

The pitch of a blade indicates the number of teeth per inch. Pitches of 14, 18, 24, and 32 teeth per inch are available. See Fig. 1-9.

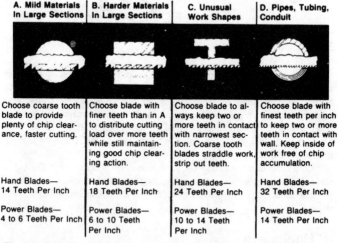

A. Mild Materials In Large Sections	B. Harder Materials In Large Sections	C. Unusual Work Shapes	D. Pipes, Tubing, Conduit
Choose coarse tooth blade to provide plenty of chip clearance, faster cutting.	Choose blade with finer teeth than in A to distribute cutting load over more teeth while still maintaining good chip clearing action.	Choose blade to always keep two or more teeth in contact with narrowest section. Coarse tooth blades straddle work, strip out teeth.	Choose blade with finest teeth per inch to keep two or more teeth in contact with wall. Keep inside of work free of chip accumulation.
Hand Blades— 14 Teeth Per Inch	Hand Blades— 18 Teeth Per Inch	Hand Blades— 24 Teeth Per Inch	Hand Blades— 32 Teeth Per Inch
Power Blades— 4 to 6 Teeth Per Inch	Power Blades— 6 to 10 Teeth Per Inch	Power Blades— 10 to 14 Teeth Per Inch	Power Blades— 14 Teeth Per Inch

Fig. 1-9. Typical uses for various pitch hacksaw blades.

Chisels

A chisel is a hard steel cutting tool that can be used for cutting and chipping any metal softer than the chisel itself. It can be used in restricted areas and for

such work as shearing rivets, or splitting seized or damaged nuts from bolts (Fig. 1-10).

The size of a *flat cold* chisel is determined by the width of the cutting edge. Lengths will vary, but chisels are seldom fewer than 5 inches or more than 8 inches long.

A chisel should be held firmly in one hand. With the other hand, the chisel head should be struck squarely with a ball-peen hammer.

When cutting square corners or slots, a special cold chisel called a *cape* chisel should be used. It is like a flat chisel except the cutting edge is very narrow. It has the same cutting angle and is held and used in the same manner as any other chisel.

Rounded or semicircular grooves and corners that have fillets should be cut with a *roundnose* chisel. This chisel is also used to recenter a drill that has moved away from its intended center.

The *diamond point* chisel is tapered square at the cutting end, then ground at an angle to provide the sharp diamond point. It is used for cutting grooves and inside sharp angles.

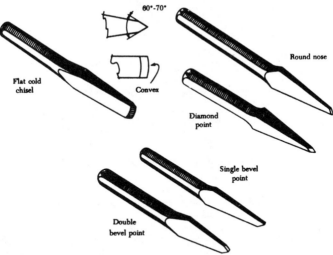

Fig. 1-10. Chisels.

Files

Files are used to square ends, file rounded corners, remove burrs and slivers from metal, straighten uneven edges, file holes and slots, and smooth rough edges. Common files are shown in Fig. 1-11.

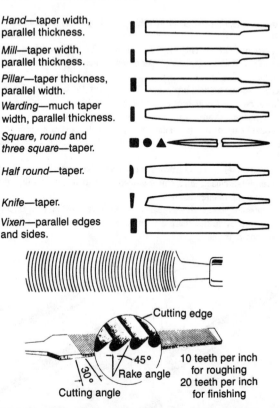

Fig. 1-11. Different files. Deep, curved single-cut tooth files (lower) have proven most satisfactory for filing aluminum.

Files are usually made in two styles: *single-cut* and *double-cut*. The single-cut file has a single row of teeth extending across the face at an angle of 65 degrees to 85 degrees with the length of the file. The size of the cuts depends on the coarseness of the file. The double-cut file has two rows of teeth that cross each other. For general work, the angle of the first row is 40 degrees to 45 degrees. The first row is generally referred to as *overcut*; and the second row as *upcut*; the upcut is somewhat finer and not so deep as the overcut.

The following methods are recommended for using files:

Crossfiling. Before attempting to use a file, place a handle on the tang of the file. This is essential for proper guiding and safe use. In moving the file endwise across the work (commonly known as *crossfiling*), grasp the handle so

that its end fits into and against the fleshy part of the palm with the thumb lying along the top of the handle in a lengthwise direction. Grasp the end of the file between the thumb and first two fingers. To prevent undue wear, relieve the pressure during the return stroke.

Drawfiling. A file is sometimes used by grasping it at each end, crosswise to the work, then moving it lengthwise with the work. When done properly, work can be finished somewhat finer than when crossfiling with the same file. In *drawfiling*, the teeth of the file produce a shearing effect. To accomplish this shearing effect, the angle at which the file is held with respect to its line of movement varies with different files, depending on the angle at which the teeth are cut. Pressure should be relieved during the backstroke.

Rounding Corners. The method used in filing a rounded surface depends upon its width and radius of the rounded surface. If the surface is narrow or only a portion of a surface is to be rounded, start the forward stroke of the file with the point of the file inclined downward at approximately a 45-degree angle. Using a rocking chair motion, finish the stroke with the heel of the file near the curved surfaced. This method allows use of the full length of the file.

Removing Burred or Slivered Edges. Practically every cutting operation on sheet metal produces burrs or slivers. These must be removed to avoid personal injury and to prevent scratching and marring of parts to be assembled. Burrs and slivers will prevent parts from fitting properly and should always be removed from the work as a matter of habit.

Particles of metal collect between the teeth of a file and might make deep scratches in the material being filed. When these particles of metal are lodged too firmly between the teeth and cannot be removed by tapping the edge of the file, remove them with a file card or wire brush. Draw the brush across the file so that the bristles pass down the gullet between the teeth.

Drilling and Countersinking

Drilling and countersinking techniques are in chapter 3.

Reamers

Reamers and reaming technique are in chapter 3.

LAYOUT AND MEASURING TOOLS

Layout and measuring devices are precision tools. They are carefully machined, accurately marked and, in many cases, are made up of very delicate parts. When using these tools, be careful not to drop, bend, or scratch them. The finished product will be no more accurate than the measurements or the layout; therefore, it is very important to understand how to read, use, and care for these tools.

Rules

Rules are made of steel and are either rigid or flexible. The flexible steel rule will bend, but it should not be bent intentionally because it might be broken rather easily (Fig. 1-12).

In aircraft work, the unit of measure most commonly used is the inch. The inch is separated into smaller parts by means of either common or decimal fraction divisions. The fractional divisions for an inch are found by dividing the inch into equal parts: halves ($1/2$), quarters ($1/4$), eighths ($1/8$), sixteenths ($1/16$), thirty-seconds ($1/32$), and sixty-fourths ($1/64$). The fractions of an inch can be expressed in decimals, called *decimal equivalents*, of an inch; for example, $1/8''$ is expressed as 0.0125 (one hundred twenty-five ten-thousandths of an inch), or more commonly, twelve and one-half thousandths. (See chart, page 232.)

Rules are manufactured with two presentations: divided or marked in common fractions; divided or marked in decimals or divisions of $0.01''$. A rule can be used either as a measuring tool or as a straightedge.

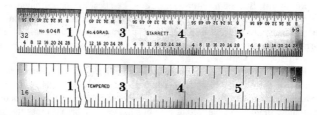

Fig. 1-12. Steel rules are available in various lengths. (Courtesy L.S. Starret Company.)

Combination Sets

The combination set (Fig. 1-13), as its name implies, is a tool that has several uses. It can be used for the same purposes as an ordinary trisquare, but it differs from the trisquare in that the head slides along the blade and can be clamped at any desired place. Combined with the *square* or *stock head* are a *level* and *scriber*. The head slides in a central groove on the blade or scale, which can be used separately as a rule.

The spirit level in the stock head makes it convenient to square a piece of material with a surface and at the same time tell whether one or the other is plumb or level. The head can be used alone as a simple level.

The combination of square head and blade can also be used as a marking gauge to scribe lines at a 45-degree angle, as a depth gauge, or as a height gauge.

Fig. 1-13. A combination set. (Courtesy L.S. Starret Company.)

Scriber

The scriber (Fig. 1-14) is used to scribe or mark lines on metal surfaces.

Fig. 1-14. A scriber.

Dividers and Calipers

Dividers have two legs tapered to a needle point and joined at the tip by a pivot. They are used to scribe circles and for transferring measurements from the rule to the work.

Calipers are used for measuring diameters and distances or for comparing distances and sizes. The most common types of calipers are the *inside* and the *outside* calipers. (See Fig. 1-15.)

Micrometer Calipers

Four micrometer calipers are each designed for a specific use: *outside*, *inside*, *depth*, and *thread*. Micrometers are available in a variety of sizes, either 0 to $1/2$ inch, 0 to 1 inch, 1 to 2 inch, 2 to 3 inch, 3 to 4 inch, 4 to 5 inch, or 5 to 6 inch sizes. Larger sizes are available.

The 0 to 1 inch outside micrometer (Fig. 1-16) is used by the mechanic more often than any other type. It might be used to measure the outside dimensions of shafts, thickness of sheet metal stock, diameter of drills, and for many other applications.

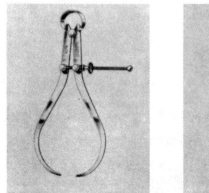
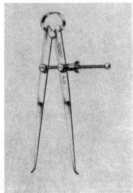

Fig. 1-15. Typical outside and inside calipers. (Courtesy L.S. Starret Company.)

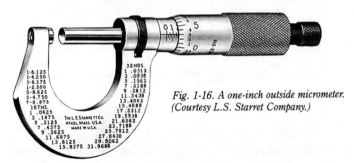

*Fig. 1-16. A one-inch outside micrometer.
(Courtesy L.S. Starret Company.)*

The smallest measurement that can be made with the use of the steel rule is one sixty-fourth of an inch in common fractions, and one one-hundredth of an inch in decimal fractions. To measure more closely than this (in thousandths and ten-thousandths of an inch), a *micrometer* is used. If a dimension given in a common fraction is to be measured with the micrometer, the fraction must be converted to its decimal equivalent.

Reading a Micrometer

Because the pitch of the screw thread on the spindle is $1/40''$, or 40 threads per inch in micrometers graduated to measure in inches, one complete revolution of the thimble advances the spindle face toward or away from the anvil face precisely $1/40''$ or .025 inch.

The reading line on the sleeve is divided into 40 equal parts by vertical lines that correspond to the number of threads on the spindle. Therefore, each verti-

cal line designates $1/40''$ or .025 inch, and every fourth line, which is longer than the others, designates hundreds of thousandths. For example: the line marked "1" represents .100 inch, the line marked "2" represents .200 inch, and the line marked "3" represents .300 inch, etc.

The beveled edge of the thimble is divided into 25 equal parts with each line representing .001 inch and every line numbered consecutively. Rotating the thimble from one of these lines to the next moves the spindle longitudinally $1/25''$ of .025 inch, or .001 inch; rotating two divisions represents .002 inch, etc. Twenty-five divisions indicate a complete revolution, .025 or $1/40''$ of an inch.

To read the micrometer in thousandths, multiply the number of vertical divisions visible on the sleeve by .025 inch, and to this add the number of thousandths indicated by the line on the thimble that coincides with the reading line on the sleeve.

Example: Refer to Fig. 1-17.

The "1" line on the sleeve is visible, representing .100".

There are 3 additional lines visible, each representing .025".

$3 \times .025'' = .075''$

Line "3" on the thimble coincides with the reading line on the sleeve, each line representing .001".

$3 \times .001'' = .003''$

The micrometer reading is .178".

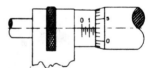

Fig. 1-17. Reading a micrometer.

SLEEVE   THIMBLE

READING .178"

TAPS AND DIES

A tap is used to cut threads on the inside of a hole, while a die is for cutting external threads on round stock. Taps and dies are made of hard-tempered steel and ground to an exact size. Four threads can be cut with standard taps and dies: *national coarse, national fine, national extra fine,* and *national pipe.*

Hand taps are usually provided in sets of three taps for each diameter and thread series. Each set contains a *taper,* a *plug,* and a *bottoming* tap. The taps in

a set are identical in diameter and cross section; the only difference is the amount of taper (Fig. 1-18).

The taper tap is used to begin the tapping process because it is tapered back for 6 to 7 threads. This tap cuts a complete thread when it is needed when tapping holes that extend through thin sections. The plug tap supplements the taper tap for tapping holes in thick stock.

The bottoming tap is not tapered. It is used to cut full threads to the bottom of a blind hole.

Dies can be classified as *adjustable round split* and *plain round split* (Fig. 1-19). The adjustable-split die has an adjusting screw that can be controlled.

Solid dies are not adjustable; therefore, several thread fits cannot be cut.

Many wrenches turn taps and dies: *T-handle*, *adjustable tap*, and *diestock* for round split dies (Fig. 1-20) are common.

Information on thread sizes, fits, types, and the like, is in the appendix.

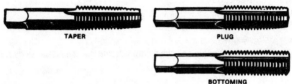

TAPER   PLUG

BOTTOMING

Fig. 1-18. Hand taps.

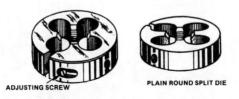

ADJUSTING SCREW   PLAIN ROUND SPLIT DIE

ADJUSTABLE ROUND SPLIT DIE

Fig. 1-19. Die types.

SHOP EQUIPMENT

Only the simpler metalworking machines, such as used in the service field, are presented in this manual. These include the powered and nonpowered metal-cutting machines, such as the various types of saws, powered and nonpowered *shears*, and *nibblers*. Also included is forming equipment (both power-driven and nonpowered), such as *brakes* and *forming rolls*, the *bar folder*, and *shrinking* and *stretching* machines. Factory equipment, such as *hydropresses*, *drop forge* machines, and *sparmills*, for example, are not described.

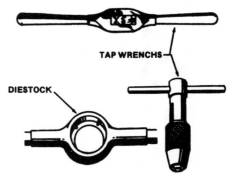

Fig. 1-20. Diestock and tap wrenches.

Holding Devices

Vises and *clamps* are tools used for holding materials of various kinds on which some type of operation is being performed. The operation and the material that is held determines which holding device is used. A typical vise is shown in Fig. 1-21.

Fig. 1-21. A machinist's vise.

Squaring Shears

Squaring shears provide a convenient means of cutting and squaring metal. Three distinctly different operations can be performed on the squaring shears: (1) cutting to a line, (2) squaring, and (3) multiple cutting to a specific size. A squaring shear is shown in chapter 2.

Throatless Shears

Throatless shears (Fig. 1-22) are best used to cut 10-gauge mild carbon sheet metal and 12-gauge stainless steel. The shear gets its name from its construction; it actually has no throat. There are no obstructions during cutting because the frame is throatless. A sheet of any length can be cut, and the metal can be turned in any direction to allow for cutting irregular shapes. The cutting blade (top blade) is operated by a hand lever.

Fig. 1-22. Throatless shears.

Bar Folder

The bar folder (Fig. 1-23) is designed for use in making bends or folds along edges of sheets. This machine is best suited for folding small hems, flanges, seams, and edges to be wired. Most bar folders have a capacity for metal up to 22 gauge thickness and 42 inches long.

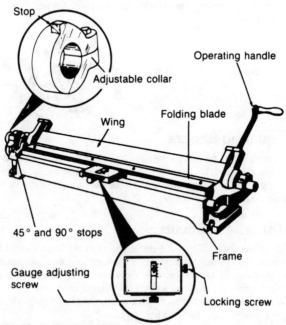

Fig. 1-23. Manually operated bar folder.

Sheet Metal Brake

The sheet metal brake (Fig. 1-24) has a much greater range of usefulness than the bar folder. Any bend formed on a bar folder can be made on the sheet metal brake. The bar folder can form a bend or edge only as wide as the depth of the jaws. In comparison, the sheet metal brake allows the sheet that is to be folded or formed to pass through the jaws from front to rear without obstruction.

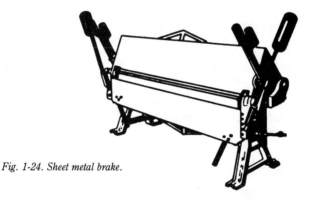

Fig. 1-24. Sheet metal brake.

Slip Roll Former

The slip roll former (Fig. 1-25) is manually operated and consists of three rolls, two housings, a base, and a handle. The handle turns the two front rolls through a system of gears enclosed in the housing. By properly adjusting the roller spacing, metal can be formed into a curve.

Fig. 1-25. Slip roll former.

Grinders

A grinding wheel is a cutting tool with a large number of cutting edges arranged so that when they become dull they break off and new cutting edges take their place.

Silicon carbide and *aluminum oxide* are the abrasives used in most grinding wheels. Silicon carbide is the cutting agent for grinding hard, brittle material, such as cast iron. It is also used in grinding aluminum, brass, bronze, and copper. Aluminum oxide is the cutting agent for grinding steel and other metals of high tensile strength.

The size of the abrasive particles used in grinding wheels is indicated by a number that corresponds to the number of meshes per linear inch in the screen through which the particles will pass. As an example, a number 30 abrasive will pass through a screen having 30 holes per linear inch, but will be retained by a smaller screen having more than 30 holes per linear inch.

A common bench grinder found in most metalworking shops is shown in Fig. 1-26. This grinder can be used to dress mushroomed heads on chisels, and points on chisels, screwdrivers, and drills. It can be used for removing excess metal from work and smoothing metal surfaces.

Fig. 1-26. A bench grinder.

As a rule, it is not good practice to grind work on the side of an abrasive wheel. When an abrasive wheel becomes worn, its cutting efficiency is reduced because of a decrease in surface speed. When a wheel becomes worn in this manner, it should be discarded and a new one installed.

Before using a bench grinder, the abrasive wheels should be checked to make sure that they are firmly held on the spindles by the flange nuts. If an abrasive wheel should come off or become loose, it could seriously injure the operator in addition to ruining the grinder.

Another hazard is loose tool rests. A loose tool rest could cause the tool or piece of work to be "grabbed" by the abrasive wheel and cause the operator's hand to come in contact with the wheel.

Goggles should always be worn when using a grinder, even if eye-shields are attached to the grinder. Goggles should fit firmly against the face and nose. This is the only way to protect eyes from the fine pieces of steel.

The abrasive wheel should be checked for cracks before using the grinder. A cracked abrasive wheel is likely to fly apart when turning at high speeds. A grinder should never be used unless it is equipped with wheel guards.

2
Materials and Fabricating

There are many different materials that go into the manufacturing of an aerospace vehicle. Some of these materials are:

- Aluminum and Aluminum alloys
- Titanium and Titanium alloys
- Magnesium and Magnesium alloys
- Steel and Steel Alloys

ALUMINUM AND ALUMINUM ALLOYS

Aluminum is one of the most widely used metals in modern aircraft construction. It is light in weight, yet some of its alloys have strengths greater than that of structural steel. It has high resistance to corrosion under the majority of service conditions. The metal can easily be worked into any form and readily accepts a wide variety of surface finishes.

Light weight is perhaps aluminum's best known characteristic. The metal weighs only about 0.1 pound per cubic inch, as compared with 0.28 for iron.

Commercially pure aluminum has a tensile strength of about 13,000 pounds per square inch. Its usefulness as a structural material in this form thus is somewhat limited. By working the metal, as by cold rolling, its strength can be approximately doubled. Much larger increases in strength can be obtained by alloying aluminum with small percentages of one or more other metals such as manganese, silicon, copper, magnesium or zinc. Like pure aluminum, the alloys are also made stronger by cold working. Some of the alloys are further strengthened and hardened by heat treatments so that today aluminum alloys having tensile strengths approaching 100,000 pounds per square inch are available.

A wide variety of mechanical characteristics, or tempers, is available in aluminum alloys through various combinations of cold work and heat treatment. In

specifying the temper for any given product, the fabricating process and the amount of cold work to which it will subject the metal should be kept in mind. In other words, the temper specified should be such that the amount of cold work the metal will receive during fabrication will develop the desired characteristics in the finished products.

When aluminum surfaces are exposed to the atmosphere, a thin invisible oxide skin forms immediately that protects the metal from further oxidation. This self-protecting characteristic gives aluminum its high resistance to corrosion. Unless exposed to some substance or condition that destroys this protective oxide coating, the metal remains fully protected against corrosion. Some alloys are less resistant to corrosion than others, particularly certain high-strength alloys. Such alloys in some forms can be effectively protected from the majority of corrosive influences, however, by cladding the exposed surface or surfaces with a thin layer of either pure aluminum or one of the more highly corrosion-resistant alloys. Trade names for some of the clad alloys are "Alclad" and "Pureclad."

The ease with which aluminum can be fabricated into any form is one of its most important assets. The metal can be cast by any method known to foundrymen; it can be rolled to any desired thickness down to foil thinner than paper; aluminum sheet can be stamped, drawn, spun or roll-formed. The metal also can be hammered or forged. There is almost no limit to the different shapes in which the metal might be extruded.

The ease and speed that aluminum can be machined is one of the important factors contributing to the use of finished aluminum parts. The metal can be turned, milled, bored, or machined at the maximum speeds of which the majority of machines are capable. Another advantage of its flexible machining characteristics is that aluminum rod and bar can readily be employed in the high-speed manufacture of parts by automatic screw-machines.

Almost any method of joining is applicable to aluminum-riveting, welding, brazing, or soldering. A wide variety of mechanical aluminum fasteners simplifies the assembly of many products. Adhesive bonding of aluminum parts is widely employed in joining aircraft components.

Alloy and Temper Designations

Aluminum alloys are available in the *cast* and *wrought* form. Aluminum *castings* are produced by pouring molten aluminum alloy into sand or metal molds. Aluminum in the *wrought* form is obtained three ways:

- *Rolling* slabs of hot aluminum through rolling mills that produce sheet, plate and bar stock.
- *Extruding* hot aluminum through dies to form channels, angles, T sections, and the like.
- *Forging* or *hammering* a heated billet of aluminum alloy between a male and female die to form the desired part.

Cast and Wrought Aluminum Alloy Designation System

A system of four-digit numerical designations is used to identify wrought aluminum and wrought aluminum alloys. The first digit indicates the alloy group as follows:

Aluminum, 99.00 percent minimum and greater.................. 1xxx
Aluminum alloys grouped by major alloying elements

    Copper 2xxx
    Manganese 3xxx
    Silicon 4xxx
    Magnesium 5xxx
    Magnesium and Silicon................................ 6xxx
    Zinc 7xxx
    Other element 8xxx
    Unused series... 9xxx

The second digit indicates modifications of the original alloy or impurity limits. The last two digits identify the aluminum alloy or indicate the aluminum purity.

Aluminum

In the first group (1xxx) for minimum aluminum purities of 99.00 percent and greater, the last two of the four digits in the designation indicate the minimum percentage. Due to its low strength, pure aluminum is seldom used in aircraft.

Aluminum Alloys

In the 2xxx through 8xxx alloy groups, the last two of the four digits in the designation have no special significance but serve only to identify the different aluminum alloys in the group. The second digit in the alloy designation indicates alloy modifications. If the second digit in the designation is zero, it indicates the original alloy; integers 1 through 9, which are assigned consecutively, indicate alloy modifications.

Temper Designation System

Where used, the temper designation follows the alloy designation and is separated from it by a dash: 7075 – T6, 2024 – T4, and the like. The temper designation consists of a letter indicating the basic temper that can be more specifically defined by the addition of one or more digits. Designations are shown in Fig. 2-1.

Nonheat-Treatable Alloys		Heat-Treatable Alloys	
Temper designation	**Definition**	**Temper designation**	**Definition**
– O	Annealed recrystallized (wrought products only) applies to softest temper of wrought products.	– O	Annealed recrystallized (wrought products only) applies to softest temper of wrought products.
– H12	Strain-hardened one-quarter-hard temper.	– T2	Annealed (castings only.)
		– T3	Solution heat-treated and cold-worked by the flattening or straightening operation.
– H14	Strain-hardened half-hard temper.		
– H16	Strain-hardened three-quarters-hard temper.		
		– T36	Solution heat-treated and cold-worked by reduction of 6 percent.
– H18	Strain-hardened full-hard temper.		
– H22	Strain-hardened and partially annealed to one-quarter-hard temper.	– T4	Solution heat-treated.
		– T42	Solution heat-treated by the user regardless of prior temper (applicable only to 2014 and 2024 alloys).
– H24	Strain-hardened and partially annealed to half-hard temper.		
– H26	Strain-hardened and partially annealed to three-quarters-hard temper.	– T5	Artificially aged only (castings only).
		– T6	Solution heat-treated and artificially aged.
– H28	Strain-hardened and partially annealed to full-hard temper.		
– H32	Strain-hardened and then stabilized. Final temper is one-quarter hard.	– T62	Solution heat-treated and aged by user regardless of prior temper (applicable only to 2014 and 2024 alloys).
– H34	Strain-hardened and then stabilized. Final temper is one-half hard.	– T351, – T451 – T3510, – T3511, – T4510, – T4511.	Solution heat-treated and stress relieved by stretching to produce a permanent set of 1 to 3 percent, depending on the product.
– H36	Strain-hardened and then stabilized. Final temper is three-quarters hard.	– T651, – T851, – T6510, – T8510, – T6511, – T8511.	Solution heat-treated, stress relieved by stretching to produce a permanent set of 1 to 3 percent, and artifically aged.
– H38	Strain-hardened and then stabilized. Final temper is full-hard.		
– H112	As fabricated; with specified mechanical property limits.	– T652	Solution heat-treated, compressed to produce a permanent set and then artificially aged.
– F	For wrought alloys; as fabricated. No mechanical properties limits. For cast alloys; as cast.	– T81	Solution heat-treated, cold-worked by the flattening or straightening operation, and then artificially aged.
		– T86	Solution heat-treated, cold-worked by reduction of 6 percent, and then artificially aged.
		– F	For wrought alloys; as fabricated. No mechanical properties limits. For cast alloys; as cast.

Fig. 2-1. Aluminum alloy temper designation chart.

CHARACTERISTICS OF ALUMINUM ALLOYS

In high-purity form, aluminum is soft and ductile. Most aircraft uses, however, require greater strength than pure aluminum affords. This is achieved in aluminum first by the addition of other elements to produce various alloys, which singly or in combination impart strength to the metal. Further strengthening is possible by means that classify the alloys roughly into two categories, *nonheat-treatable* and *heat-treatable*.

Nonheat-treatable alloys. The initial strength of alloys in this group depends upon the hardening effect of elements such as manganese, silicon, iron, and magnesium, singly or in various combinations. The nonheat-treatable alloys are usually designated, therefore, in the 1000, 3000, 4000, or 5000

series. Because these alloys are work-hardenable, further strengthening is made possible by various degrees of cold working, denoted by the "H" series of tempers. Alloys containing appreciable amounts of magnesium when supplied in strain-hardened tempers are usually given a final elevated-temperature treatment called *stabilizing* to ensure stability of properties.

Heat-treatable alloys. The initial strength of alloys in this group is enhanced by the addition of alloying elements such as copper, magnesium, zinc, and silicon. Because these elements singly or in various combinations show increasing solid solubility in aluminum with increasing temperature, it is possible to subject them to thermal treatments that will impart pronounced strengthening.

The first step, called *heat treatment* or *solution heat treatment*, is an elevated-temperature process designed to put the soluble element or elements in solid solution. This is followed by rapid quenching, usually in water, which momentarily "freezes" the structure and for a short time renders the alloy very workable; selected fabricators retain this more workable structure by storing the alloys at below freezing temperatures until initiating the formation process, *ice box rivets* are a typical example. At room or elevated temperatures the alloys are unstable after quenching, however, and precipitation of the constituents from the super-saturated solution begins.

After a period of several days at room temperature, termed *aging* or *room-temperature precipitation*, the alloy is considerably stronger. Many alloys approach a stable condition at room temperature, but selected alloys, particularly those containing magnesium and silicon or magnesium and zinc continue to age-harden for long periods of time at room temperature.

By heating for a specified time at slightly elevated temperatures, even further strengthening is possible and properties are stabilized, called *artificial aging* or *precipitation hardening*. By the proper combination of solution heat treatment, quenching, cold working and artificial aging, the highest strengths are obtained.

Clad Alloys. The heat-treatable alloys in which copper or zinc are major alloying constituents are less resistant to corrosive attack than the majority of nonheat-treatable alloys. To increase the corrosion resistance of these alloys in sheet and plate form they are often clad with high-purity aluminum, a low magnesium-silicon alloy, or an alloy containing 1 percent zinc. The cladding, usually from $2^1/2$ to 5 percent of the total thickness on each side, not only protects the composite due to its own inherently excellent corrosion resistance, but also exerts a galvanic effect that further protects the core material.

Annealing Characteristics

All wrought aluminum alloys are available in annealed form. In addition, it might be desirable to anneal an alloy from any other initial temper, after working, or between successive stages of working, such as deep drawing.

Typical Uses of Aluminum and Its Alloys

Various aluminum alloys are used for aircraft fabrication:

1000 series. Aluminum of 99 percent or higher purity has practically no application in the aerospace industry. These alloys are characterized by excellent corrosion resistance, high thermal and electrical conductivity, low mechanical properties, and excellent workability. Moderate increases in strength can be obtained by strain-hardening. Soft, 1100 rivets are used in nonstructural applications.

2000 series. Copper is the principal alloying element in this group. These alloys require solution heat-treatment to obtain optimum properties; in the heat-treated condition mechanical properties are similar to, and sometimes exceed, those of mild steel. In some instances artificial aging is employed to further increase the mechanical properties. This treatment materially increases yield strength. These alloys in the form of sheet are usually clad with a high-purity alloy. Alloy 2024 is perhaps the best known and most widely used aircraft alloy. Most aircraft rivets are of alloy 2117.

3000 series. Manganese is the major alloying element of alloys in this group, which are generally nonheat-treatable. One of these is 3003, which has limited use as a general-purpose alloy for moderate-strength applications requiring good workability, such as cowlings and nonstructural parts. Alloy 3003 is easy to weld.

4000 series. This alloy series is seldom used in the aerospace industry.

5000 series. Magnesium is one of the most effective and widely used alloying elements for aluminum. When it is used as the major alloying element, or with manganese, the result is a moderate to high strength nonheat-treatable alloy. Alloys in this series possess good welding characteristics and good resistance to corrosion in various atmospheres. It is widely used for the fabrication of tanks and fluid lines.

6000 series. Alloys in this group contain silicon and magnesium in approximate proportions to form magnesium silicide, thus making them heat-treatable. The major alloy in this series is 6061, one of the most versatile of the heat-treatable alloys. Though less strong than most of the 2000 or 7000 alloys, the magnesium-silicon (or magnesium-silicide) alloys possess good formability and corrosion resistance, with medium strength.

7000 series. Zinc is the major alloying element in this group, and when coupled with a smaller percentage of magnesium results in heat-treatable alloys of very high strength. Usually other elements, such as copper and chromium, are also added in small quantities. The outstanding member of this group is 7075, which is among the highest strength alloys available and is used in airframe structures and for highly stressed parts.

Heat Treatment of Aluminum Alloys

Heat treatment of aluminum alloys is summarized in Fig. 2-2.

Alloy	Solution heat-treatment			Precipitation heat-treatment		
	Temp., °F	Quench	Temper desig.	Temp., °F	Time of aging	Temper desig.
2017	930-950	Cold water	T4			T
2117	930-950	Cold water	T4			T
2024	910-930	Cold water	T4			T
6053	960-980	Water	T4	445-455	1-2 hr	T5
				or		
				345-355	8 hr	T6
6061	960-980	Water	T4	315-325	18 hr	T6
				or		
				345-355	8 hr	T6
7075	870	Water		250	24 hr	T6

Fig. 2-2. Conditions for heat treatment of aluminum alloys. (For information only. Not to be used for actual heat treatment. Heating times vary with the product, type of furnace, and thickness of material. Quenching is normally in cold water, although hot water or air blast can be used for bulky sections.)

Identification of Aluminum

To provide a visual means for identifying the various grades of aluminum and aluminum alloys, such metals are usually marked with symbols such as *Government Specification Number*, the temper or condition furnished, or the commercial code marking. Plate and sheet are usually marked with specification numbers or code markings in rows approximately 6 inches apart. Tubes, bars, rods, and extruded shapes are marked with specification numbers or code markings continuously or at intervals of 3 to 5 feet along the length of each piece. The commercial code marking consists of a number that identifies the particular composition of the alloy. In addition, letter suffixes designate the temper designation.

FORMING ALUMINUM ALLOYS
Forming at the Factory

Parts are formed at the factory on large presses or by drop hammers equipped with dies of the correct shape. Every part is planned by factory engineers, who set up specifications for the materials to be used so that the finished part will have the correct temper when it leaves the machines. A layout for each part is prepared by factory draftsmen.

The verb "form" means to shape or mold into a different shape or in a particular pattern, and thus would include even casting. However, in most metal-working terminology, "forming" is generally understood to mean changing the shape by bending and deforming solid metal.

In the case of aluminum this is usually done at room temperature. In metal-working, "forming" includes *bending, brake forming, stretch forming, roll forming, drawing, spinning, shear forming, flexible die forming* and *high velocity forming.*

Other "forming" methods, such as *machining, extruding, forging,* and *casting* do change the shape of the metal, by metal removal or at elevated temperatures. However, these processes employ different tooling and/or equipment.

Manufacturers form aluminum by rolling, drawing, extruding and forging to create the basic aluminum shapes from which the metalworker in turn makes all types of end products. As a group, the aluminum products fabricated from ingot by the producers are called *mill products.*

The principal mill products utilized by the metalworker in forming are *sheet, plate, rod, bar, wire,* and *tube.* Sheet thickness ranges from 0.006 through 0.249 inch; plate is 0.250 inch or more; rod is $3/8$ inch diameter or greater; bar is rectangular, hexagonal, or octagonal in cross section, having at least one perpendicular distance between faces of $3/8$ inch or greater. Wire is 0.374 inch or less.

Most parts are formed without annealing the metal, but if extensive forming operations, such as *deep draws* (large folds) or complex curves are planned, the metal is in the dead soft or annealed condition. During the forming of some complex parts, operations might have to be stopped and the metal annealed before the process can be continued or completed. Alloy 2024 in the "O" condition can be formed into almost any shape by the common forming operations, but it must be heat treated afterward.

Making Straight Line Bends

Because forming at the factory, which was briefly discussed previously, involves specialized equipment and techniques, it is beyond the scope of this handbook. However, an example of straight line bends is appropriate.

When forming straight bends, the thickness of the material, its alloy composition, and its temper condition must be considered. Generally speaking, the thinner the material, the sharper it can be bent (the smaller the radius of bend), and the softer the material, the sharper the bend. Other factors that must be considered when making straight line bends are bend allowance, setback, and brake or sight line.

The *radius of bend* of a sheet of material is the radius of the bend as measured on the inside of the curved materials. The minimum radius of bend of a sheet of material is the sharpest curve, or bend, to which the sheet can be bent without critically weakening the metal at the bend. If the radius of bend is too small, stresses and strains will weaken the metal and might result in cracking.

A minimum radius of bend is specified for each type of aircraft sheet metal. The kind of material, thickness, and temper condition of the sheet are factors

affecting the minimum radius. Annealed sheet can be bent to a radius approximately equal to its thickness. Stainless steel and 2024-T aluminum alloy require a fairly large bend radius.

A general rule for minimum bend radii is:

1 × thickness for O temper.
2¹/₂ × thickness for T4 temper.
3 × thickness for T3 temper.

Bend Allowance

When making a bend or fold in a sheet of metal, the bend allowance must be calculated. Bend allowance is the length of material required for the bend. This amount of metal must be added to the overall length of the layout pattern to assure adequate metal for the bend (Fig. 2-3).

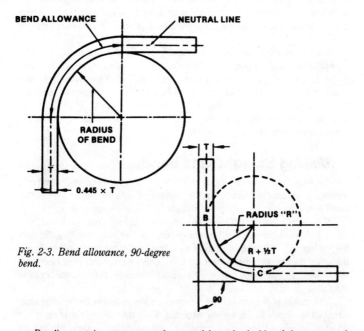

Fig. 2-3. Bend allowance, 90-degree bend.

Bending a strip compresses the material on the inside of the curve and stretches the material on the outside of the curve. However, at some distance between these two extremes lies a space that is not affected by either force. This is known as the *neutral line* or *neutral axis* and occurs at a distance

approximately 0.445 times the metal thickness (0.455 × T) from the inside of the radius of the bend.

When bending metal to exact dimensions, the length of the neutral line must be determined so that sufficient material can be allowed for the bend. To save time in calculation of the bend allowance, formulas and charts for various angles, radii of bends, material thicknesses, and other factors have been established.

By experimentation with actual bends in metals, aircraft engineers have found that accurate bending results could be obtained by using the following formula for any degree of bend from 1 degree to 180 degrees:

Bend allowance = $(0.01743 \times R + 0.0078 \times T) \times N$

where:

R = The desired bend radius,
T = Thickness of the material, and
N = Number of degrees of bend.

This formula may be used in the absence of a bend allowance chart. To determine bend allowance for any degree of bend by use of the chart (Fig. 2-4), find the allowance per degree for the number of degrees in the bend.

Radius of bend is given as a decimal fraction on the top line of the chart. Bend allowance is given directly below the radius figures. The top number in each case is the bend allowance for a 90 degree angle, whereas the lower placed number is for a 1 degree angle. Material thickness is given in the left column of the chart.

To find the bend allowance when the sheet thickness is 0.051″, the radius of bend is ¹/₄″ (0.250″), and the bend is to be 90 degrees. Reading across the top of the bend allowance chart, find the column for a radius of bend of 0.250″. Now find the block in this column that is opposite the gauge of 0.051 in the column at left. The upper number in the block is 0.428, the correct bend allowance in inches for a 90-degree bend (0.428″ bend allowance).

If the bend is to be other than 90 degrees, use the lower number in the block (the bend allowance for 1 degree) and compute the bend allowance. The lower number in this case is 0.004756. Therefore, if the bend is to be 120 degrees, the total bend allowance in inches will be 120 × 0.004756, which equals 0.5707″.

When bending a piece of sheet stock, it is necessary to know the starting and ending points of the bend so that the length of the "flat" of the stock can be determined. Two factors are important in determining this, the radius of bend and the thickness of the material.

Note that *setback* is the distance from the bend tangent line to the mold point. The *mold point* is the point of intersection of the lines extending from the outside surfaces, whereas the *bend tangent lines* are the starting and end points

RADIUS GAGE	.031	.063	.094	.125	.156	.188	.219	.250	.281	.313	.344	.375	.438	.500
.020	.042 / .000493	.113 / .001231	.161 / .001792	.210 / .002333	.259 / .002874	.309 / .003433	.358 / .003974	.406 / .004515	.455 / .005056	.505 / .005614	.554 / .006155	.603 / .006695	.702 / .007795	.799 / .008887
.025	.044 / .000734	.116 / .001294	.165 / .001835	.214 / .002376	.263 / .002917	.313 / .003476	.362 / .004017	.410 / .004558	.459 / .005098	.509 / .005657	.558 / .006198	.607 / .006738	.705 / .007838	.803 / .008920
.028	.048 / .000759	.119 / .001318	.167 / .001859	.216 / .002400	.265 / .002941	.315 / .003499	.364 / .004040	.412 / .004581	.461 / .005122	.511 / .005680	.560 / .006221	.609 / .006762	.708 / .007862	.805 / .007863
.032	.071 / .000787	.121 / .001345	.170 / .001886	.218 / .002427	.267 / .002968	.317 / .003526	.344 / .004067	.415 / .004608	.463 / .005149	.514 / .005708	.562 / .006249	.611 / .006789	.710 / .007889	.807 / .008971
.038	.075 / .000837	.126 / .001398	.174 / .001937	.223 / .002478	.272 / .003019	.322 / .003577	.371 / .004118	.419 / .004659	.468 / .005200	.518 / .005758	.567 / .006299	.616 / .006840	.715 / .007940	.812 / .009021
.040	.077 / .000853	.127 / .001411	.176 / .001952	.224 / .002493	.273 / .003034	.323 / .003593	.372 / .004134	.421 / .004675	.469 / .005215	.520 / .005774	.569 / .006315	.617 / .006856	.716 / .007955	.813 / .009037
.051		.134 / .001413	.183 / .002034	.232 / .002575	.280 / .003116	.331 / .003675	.379 / .004215	.428 / .004756	.477 / .005297	.527 / .005855	.576 / .006397	.624 / .006934	.723 / .008037	.821 / .009119
.044	.144 / .001595		.192 / .002136	.241 / .002675	.290 / .003218	.340 / .003776	.389 / .004317	.437 / .004858	.486 / .005399	.536 / .005957	.585 / .006498	.634 / .007039	.732 / .008138	.830 / .009220
.072			.198 / .002202	.247 / .002743	.296 / .003284	.346 / .003842	.394 / .004283	.443 / .004924	.492 / .005465	.542 / .006023	.591 / .006564	.639 / .007105	.738 / .008205	.836 / .009287
.078			.202 / .002249	.251 / .002790	.300 / .003331	.350 / .003889	.399 / .004430	.447 / .004963	.496 / .005512	.546 / .006070	.595 / .006611	.644 / .007152	.745 / .008252	.840 / .009333
.081			.204 / .002272	.253 / .002813	.302 / .003354	.352 / .003912	.401 / .004453	.449 / .004969	.498 / .005535	.548 / .006094	.598 / .006635	.646 / .007176	.745 / .008275	.842 / .009357
.091			.212 / .002350	.260 / .002891	.309 / .003432	.359 / .003990	.408 / .004531	.456 / .005072	.505 / .005613	.555 / .006172	.604 / .006713	.653 / .007254	.752 / .008353	.849 / .009435
.094			.214 / .002374	.262 / .002914	.311 / .003455	.361 / .004014	.410 / .004555	.459 / .005096	.507 / .005637	.558 / .006195	.606 / .006736	.655 / .007277	.754 / .008376	.851 / .009458
.102				.268 / .002977	.317 / .003518	.367 / .004076	.416 / .004617	.464 / .005158	.513 / .005699	.563 / .006257	.612 / .006798	.661 / .007339	.760 / .008439	.857 / .009521
.109				.273 / .003031	.321 / .003572	.371 / .004131	.420 / .004672	.469 / .005213	.518 / .005754	.568 / .006312	.617 / .006853	.665 / .007394	.764 / .008493	.862 / .009575
.125				.284 / .003156	.333 / .003697	.383 / .004256	.432 / .004797	.480 / .005338	.529 / .005878	.579 / .006437	.628 / .006978	.677 / .007519	.776 / .008618	.873 / .009700
.156					.355 / .003939	.405 / .004497	.453 / .005038	.502 / .005579	.551 / .006120	.601 / .006679	.650 / .007220	.698 / .007761	.797 / .008860	.895 / .009942
.188						.417 / .004747	.476 / .005288	.525 / .005829	.573 / .006370	.624 / .006928	.672 / .007469	.721 / .008010	.820 / .009109	.917 / .010191
.250								.568 / .006313	.617 / .006853	.667 / .007412	.716 / .007953	.764 / .008494	.843 / .009593	.961 / .010673

Fig. 2-4. Bend allowance chart.

of the bend. Also note that setback is the same for the vertical flat and the horizontal flat.

To calculate the setback for a 90-degree bend, merely add the inside radius of the bend to the thickness of the sheet stock:

Setback = $R + T$. (Fig. 2-5)

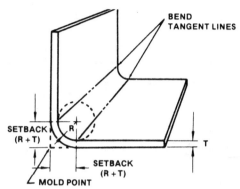

Fig. 2-5. Setback, 90-degree bend.

To calculate setback for angles larger or smaller than 90 degrees, consult standard setback charts or K chart (Fig. 2-6) for a value called K, and then substitute this value in the formula,

Setback = $K(R + T)$.

The value for K varies with the number of degrees in the bend. For example:

Calculate the setback for a 120-degree bend with a radius of bend of 0.125" for a sheet 0.032" thick;

$$\begin{aligned}
\text{Setback} &= K(R + T) \\
&= 1.7320 \, (0.125 + 0.032) \\
&= 0.272"
\end{aligned}$$

Brake or Sight Line

The brake or sight line is the mark on a flat sheet that is set even with the nose of the radius bar of the cornice brake and serves as guide when bending. The brake line can be located by measuring out one radius from the bend tangent line closest to the end that is to be inserted under the nose of the brake or against the radius form block. The nose of the brake or radius bar should fall directly over the brake or sight line as shown in Fig. 2-7.

A	K	A	K	A	K
1°	.00873	61°	.58904	121°	1.7675
2°	.01745	62°	.60086	122°	1.8040
3°	.02618	63°	.61280	123°	1.8418
4°	.03492	64°	.62487	124°	1.8807
5°	.04366	65°	.63707	125°	1.9210
6°	.05241	66°	.64941	126°	1.9626
7°	.06116	67°	.66188	127°	2.0057
8°	.06993	68°	.67451	128°	2.0503
9°	.07870	69°	.68728	129°	2.0965
10°	.08749	70°	.70021	130°	2.1445
11°	.09629	71°	.71329	131°	2.1943
12°	.10510	72°	.72654	132°	2.2460
13°	.11393	73°	.73996	133°	2.2998
14°	.12278	74°	.75355	134°	2.3558
15°	.13165	75°	.76733	135°	2.4142
16°	.14054	76°	.78128	136°	2.4751
17°	.14945	77°	.79543	137°	2.5386
18°	.15838	78°	.80978	138°	2.6051
19°	.16734	79°	.82434	139°	2.6746
20°	.17633	80°	.83910	140°	2.7475
21°	.18534	81°	.85408	141°	2.8239
22°	.19438	82°	.86929	142°	2.9042
23°	.20345	83°	.88477	143°	2.9987
24°	.21256	84°	.90040	144°	3.0777
25°	.22169	85°	.91633	145°	3.1716
26°	.23087	86°	.93251	146°	3.2708
27°	.24008	87°	.94898	147°	3.3759
28°	.24933	88°	.96569	148°	3.4874
29°	.25862	89°	.98270	149°	3.6059
30°	.26795	90°	1.0000C	150°	3.7320

A	K	A	K	A	K
31°	.27732	91°	1.0176	151°	3.8667
32°	.28674	92°	1.0355	152°	4.0108
33°	.29621	93°	1.0538	153°	4.1653
34°	.30573	94°	1.0724	154°	4.3315
35°	.31530	95°	1.0913	155°	4.5107
36°	.32492	96°	1.1106	156°	4.7046
37°	.33459	97°	1.1303	157°	4.9151
38°	.34433	98°	1.1504	158°	5.1455
39°	.35412	99°	1.1708	159°	5.3995
40°	.36397	100°	1.1917	160°	5.6713
41°	.37388	101°	1.2131	161°	5.9758
42°	.38386	102°	1.2349	162°	6.3137
43°	.39391	103°	1.2572	163°	6.6911
44°	.40403	104°	1.2799	164°	7.1154
45°	.41421	105°	1.3032	165°	7.5957
46°	.42447	106°	1.3270	166°	8.1443
47°	.43481	107°	1.3514	167°	8.7769
48°	.44523	108°	1.3764	168°	9.5144
49°	.45573	109°	1.4019	169°	10.385
50°	.46631	110°	1.4281	170°	11.430
51°	.47697	111°	1.4550	171°	12.706
52°	.48773	112°	1.4826	172°	14.301
53°	.49858	113°	1.5108	173°	16.350
54°	.50952	114°	1.5399	174°	19.081
55°	.52057	115°	1.5697	175°	22.904
56°	.53171	116°	1.6003	176°	26.636
57°	.54295	117°	1.6318	177°	38.188
58°	.55431	118°	1.6643	178°	57.290
59°	.56577	119°	1.6977	179°	114.590
60°	.57735	120°	1.7320	180°	Infinite

Fig. 2-6. Setback, (K) chart.

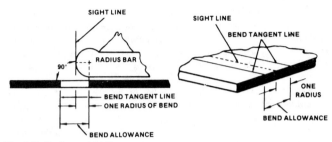

Fig. 2-7. Brake or sight line.

MAKING LAYOUTS

It is wise to make a layout or pattern of the part before forming it to reduce wasted material and to get a greater degree of accuracy in the finished part. Where straight angle bends are concerned, correct allowances must be made for setback and bend allowance.

Relief Holes

Wherever two bends intersect, material must be removed to make room for the material contained in the flanges. Holes are therefore drilled at the intersection. These holes, called *relief holes* (Fig. 2-8), prevent strains from being set up at the intersection of the inside bend tangent lines that would cause the metal to crack. Relief holes also provide a neatly trimmed corner from which excess material can be trimmed.

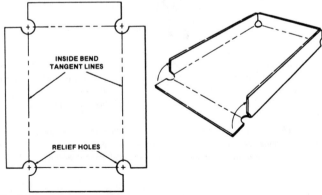

Fig. 2-8. Locating relief holes.

The size of a relief hole varies with thickness of the material. Size should be not less than 1/8″ diameter for aluminum alloy sheet stock up to and including 0.064″ thick, or 3/16″ for stock ranging from 0.072″ to 0.128″ thickness. The most common method of determining the diameter of a relief hole is to use the radius of bend for this dimension, provided it is not less than the minimum allowance (1/8″).

Relief holes must touch the intersection of the inside bend tangent lines. To allow for possible error in bending, make the relief holes so they will extend 1/32″ to 1/16″ behind the inside end tangent lines. It is good practice to use the intersection of these lines as the center for the holes. The line on the inside of the curve is cut at an angle toward the relief holes to allow for the stretching of the inside flange.

Miscellaneous Shop Equipment and Procedures

Selected pieces of shop equipment are presented in chapter 1. Figure 2-9 shows a hand operated brake for bending sheet metal. Larger brakes are power operated.

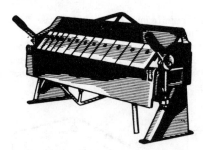

Fig. 2-9. Hand operated brake.

Bends of a more complicated design, like a sheet-metal rib having flanges around its contour, should be made over a form block shaped to fit the inside contour of the finished part. Bending the flanges over this die can be accomplished by *hand forming*, a slow but practical method for experimental work (Fig. 2-10).

Machining involves all forms of cutting, whether performed on sheet stock, castings, or extrusions, and involves such operations as shearing (Fig. 2-11), sawing, routing, lathe and millwork, and such hand operations as drilling, tapping, and reaming.

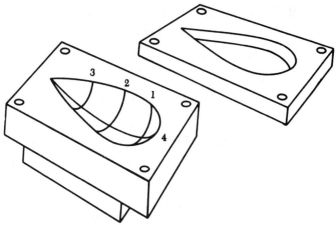

Fig. 2-10. A simple form block and hold down plate for hand forming. A speedier and better production is the use of the hydropress.

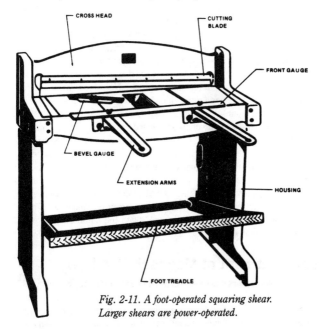

Fig. 2-11. A foot-operated squaring shear.
Larger shears are power-operated.

MAGNESIUM AND MAGNESIUM ALLOYS

Magnesium, the world's lightest structural metal, is a silvery-white material weighing only two-thirds as much as aluminum. Magnesium does not possess sufficient strength in its pure state for structural uses, but when alloyed with zinc, aluminum, and manganese it produces an alloy having the highest strength-to-weight ratio of any of the commonly used metals.

Some of today's aircraft require in excess of one-half ton of this metal for use in hundreds of vital spots. Selected wing panels are fabricated entirely from magnesium alloys, weigh 18 percent less than standard aluminum panels, and have flown hundreds of satisfactory hours. Among the aircraft parts that have been made from magnesium with a substantial savings in weight are nosewheel doors, flap cover skins, aileron cover skins, oil tanks, floorings, fuselage parts, wingtips, engine nacelles, instrument panels, radio antenna masts, hydraulic fluid tanks, oxygen bottle cases, ducts, and seats.

Magnesium alloys possess good casting characteristics. Their properties compare favorably with those of cast aluminum. In forging, hydraulic presses are ordinarily used, although, under certain conditions, forging can be accomplished in mechanical presses or with drop hammers.

Magnesium alloys are subject to such treatments as annealing, quenching, solution heat treatment, aging, and stabilizing. Sheet and plate magnesium are annealed at the rolling mill. The solution heat treatment is used to put as much of the alloying ingredients as possible into solid solution, which results in high tensile strength and maximum ductility. Aging is applied to castings following heat treatment where maximum hardness and yield strength are desired.

Magnesium embodies fire hazards of an unpredictable nature. When in large sections, high thermal conductivity makes it difficult to ignite and prevents it from burning; it will not burn until the melting point is reached, which is 1,204°F. However, magnesium dust and fine chips are ignited easily. Precautions must be taken to avoid this if possible. Should a fire occur, it can be extinguished with an extinguishing powder, such as powdered soapstone, or graphite powder. Water or any standard liquid or foam fire extinguishers cause magnesium to burn more rapidly and can cause explosions.

Magnesium alloys produced in the United States consist of magnesium alloyed with varying proportions of aluminum, manganese, and zinc. These alloys are designated by a letter of the alphabet, with the number 1 indicating high purity and maximum corrosion resistance.

Heat Treatment of Magnesium Alloys

Magnesium alloy castings respond readily to heat treatment, and about 95 percent of the magnesium used in aircraft construction is in the cast form. Heat treatment of magnesium alloy castings is similar to heat treatment of aluminum alloys because there are two types of heat treatment: *solution* and *precipitation*

(aging). Magnesium, however, develops a negligible change in its properties when allowed to age naturally at room temperatures.

TITANIUM AND TITANIUM ALLOYS

In aircraft construction and repair, titanium is used for fuselage skins, engine shrouds, firewalls, longerons, frames, fittings, air ducts, and fasteners. Titanium is used for making compressor disks, spacer rings, compressor blades and vanes, through bolts, turbine housings and liners, and miscellaneous hardware for turbine engines.

Titanium falls between aluminum and stainless steel in terms of elasticity, density, and elevated temperature strength. It has a melting point of from 2,730 to 3,155°F, low thermal conductivity, and a low coefficient of expansion. It is light, strong, and resistant to stress-corrosion cracking. Titanium is approximately 60 percent heavier than aluminum and about 50 percent lighter than stainless steel.

Because of the high melting point of titanium, high-temperature properties are disappointing. The ultimate yield strength of titanium drops rapidly above 800°F. The absorption of oxygen and nitrogen from the air at temperatures above 1,000°F makes the metal so brittle on long exposure that it soon becomes worthless. However, titanium does have some merit for short-time exposure up to 3,000°F where strength is not important. Aircraft firewalls demand this requirement.

Titanium is nonmagnetic and has an electrical resistance comparable to that of stainless steel. Some of the base alloys of titanium are quite hard. Heat treating and alloying do not develop the hardness of titanium to the high levels of some of the heat-treated alloys of steel. A heat-treatable titanium alloy was only recently developed. Prior to the development of this alloy, heating and rolling was the only method of forming that could be accomplished. However, it is possible to form the new alloy in the soft condition and heat treat it for hardness.

Iron, molybdenum, and chromium are used to stabilize titanium and produce alloys that will quench harden and age harden. The addition of these metals also adds ductility. The fatigue resistance of titanium is greater than that of aluminum or steel.

Titanium Designations

The A-B-C classification of titanium alloys was established to provide a convenient and simple means of describing all titanium alloys. Titanium and titanium alloys possess three basic crystals, A *(alpha)*, B *(beta)*, and C *(combined alpha and beta)*, that have specific characteristics:

A (alpha): all-around performance; good weldability; tough and strong both cold and hot, and resistant to oxidation.

B (beta): bendability; excellent bend ductility; strong both cold and hot, but vulnerable to contamination.

C (combined alpha and beta for compromise performances): strong when cold and warm, but weak when hot; good bendability; moderate contamination resistance; excellent forgeability.

Titanium is manufactured for commercial use in two basic compositions: *commercially pure* and *alloyed*. A-55 is an example of a commercially pure titanium; it has a yield strength of 55,000 to 80,000 psi and is a general-purpose grade for moderate to severe forming. It is sometimes used for nonstructural aircraft parts and for all types of corrosion resistant applications, such as tubing.

Type A-70 titanium is closely related to type A-55, but has a yield strength of 70,000 to 95,000 psi. It is used where higher strength is required, and it is specified for many moderately stressed aircraft parts. For many corrosion applications, it is used interchangeably with type A-55. Type A-55 and type A-70 are weldable.

One of the widely used titanium-base alloys is C-110M. It is used for primary structural members and aircraft skin, has 110,000 psi minimum yield strength, and contains 8 percent manganese.

Type A-110AT is a titanium alloy that contains 5 percent aluminum and 2.5 percent tin. It also has a high minimum yield strength at elevated temperatures with the excellent welding characteristics inherent in alpha-type titanium alloys.

Corrosion Characteristics

The corrosion resistance of titanium deserves special mention. The resistance of the metal to corrosion is caused by the formation of a protective surface film of stable oxide or chemi-absorbed oxygen. Film is often produced by the presence of oxygen and oxidizing agents.

Titanium corrosion is uniform. There is little evidence of pitting or other serious forms of localized attack. Normally, it is not subject to stress corrosion, corrosion fatigue, intergranular corrosion, or galvanic corrosion. Its corrosion resistance is equal or superior to 18-8 stainless steel.

Treatment of Titanium

Titanium is heat treated for the following purposes:

- Relief of stresses set up during cold forming or machining.
- Annealing after hot working or cold working, or to provide maximum ductility for subsequent cold working.
- Thermal hardening to improve strength.

FERROUS AIRCRAFT METALS

Ferrous applies to the group of metals having iron as their principal constituent.

Identification

If carbon is added to iron, in percentages ranging up to approximately 1 percent, the product is vastly superior to iron alone and is classified as *carbon steel*. Carbon steel forms the base of those alloy steels produced by combining carbon steel with other elements known to improve the properties of steel. A base metal, such as iron, to which small quantities of other metals have been added is called an *alloy*. The addition of other metals changes or improves the chemical or physical properties of the base metal for a particular use.

The steel classification of the SAE (Society of Automotive Engineers) is used in specifications for all high-grade steels used in automotive and aircraft construction. A numerical index system identifies the composition of SAE steels.

Each SAE number consists of a group of digits: the first digit represents the type of steel; the second, the percentage of the principal alloying element; and, usually, the last two or three digits, the percentage, in hundredths of 1 percent, of carbon in the alloy. For example, the SAE number 4130 indicates a molybdenum steel containing 1 percent molybdenum and 0.30 percent carbon.

Type of Steel	Classification
Carbon	1xxx
Nickel	2xxx
Nickel-chromium	3xxx
Molybdenum	4xxx
Chromium	5xxx
Chromium-vanadium	6xxx
Tungsten	7xxx
Silicon-manganese	9xxx

SAE numerical index

Metal stock is manufactured in several forms and shapes, including sheets, bars, rods, tubings, extrusions, forgings, and castings. Sheet metal is made in a number of sizes and thicknesses. Specifications designate thicknesses in thousandths of an inch. Bars and rods are supplied in a variety of shapes, such as round, square, rectangular, hexagonal, and octagonal. Tubing can be obtained in round, oval, rectangular, or streamlined shapes. The size of tubing is generally specified by outside diameter and wall thickness.

The sheet metal is usually formed cold in such machines as presses, bending brakes, drawbenches, or rolls. Forgings are shaped or formed by pressing

or hammering heated metal in dies. Castings are produced by pouring molten metal into molds. The casting is finished by machining.

Types, Characteristics, and Uses of Alloyed Steels

Steel that contains carbon in percentages ranging from 0.10 to 0.30 percent is *low-carbon* steel. The equivalent SAE numbers range from 1010 to 1030. Steels of this grade are used for making such items as safety wire, selected nuts, cable bushings, or threaded rod ends. This steel in sheet form is used for secondary structural parts and clamps, and in tubular form for moderately stressed structural parts.

Steel that contains carbon in percentages ranging from 0.30 to 0.50 percent is *medium-carbon* steel. This steel is especially adaptable for machining or forging, and where surface hardness is desirable. Selected rod ends and light forgings are made from SAE 1035 steel.

Steel that contains carbon in percentages ranging from 0.50 to 1.05 percent is *high-carbon* steel. The addition of other elements in varying quantities add to the hardness of this steel. In the fully heat-treated condition, it is very hard, will withstand high shear and wear, and will have minor deformation. It has limited use in aircraft. SAE 1095 in sheet form is used for making flat springs and in wire form for making coil springs.

The various *nickel* steels are produced by combining nickel with carbon steel. Steels containing from 3 to 3.75 percent nickel are commonly used. Nickel increases the hardness, tensile strength, and elastic limit of steel without appreciably decreasing the ductility. It also intensifies the hardening effect of heat treatment. SAE 2330 steel is used extensively for aircraft parts, such as bolts, terminals, keys, clevises, and pins.

Chromium steel has high hardness, strength, and corrosion-resistant properties, and is particularly adaptable for heat-treated forgings that require greater toughness and strength than can be obtained in plain carbon steel. Chromium steel can be used for such articles as the balls and rollers of antifriction bearings.

Chrome-nickel (*stainless*) steels are the corrosion-resistant metals. The anticorrosive degree of this steel is determined by the surface condition of the metal as well as by the composition, temperature, and concentration of the corrosive agent.

The principal alloy of stainless steel is chromium. The corrosion-resistant steel most often used in aircraft construction is known as 18-8 steel because it is 18 percent chromium and 8 percent nickel. One distinctive feature of 18-8 steel is that its strength can be increased by coldworking.

Stainless steel can be rolled, drawn, bent, or formed to any shape.

Because these steels expand about 50 percent more than mild steel and conduct heat only about 40 percent as rapidly, they are more difficult to weld. Stainless steel can be used for almost any part of an aircraft. Some of its common applications are in the fabrication of exhaust collectors, stacks and manifolds, structural and machine parts, springs, castings, tie rods, and control cables.

Chrome-vanadium steels are made of approximately 18 percent vanadium and about 1 percent chromium. When heat treated, they have strength, toughness, and resistance to wear and fatigue. A special grade of this steel in sheet form can be cold formed into intricate shapes. It can be folded and flattened without signs of breaking or failure. SAE 6150 is used for making springs, while chrome-vanadium with high-carbon content, SAE 6195, is used for ball and roller bearings.

Molybdenum in small percentages is used in combination with chromium to form *chrome-molybdenum* steel, which has various uses in aircraft. Molybdenum is a strong alloying element that raises the ultimate strength of steel without affecting ductility or workability. Molybdenum steels are tough and wear resistant, and they harden throughout when heat treated. They are especially adaptable for welding and, for this reason, are used principally for welded structural parts and assemblies. This type steel has practically replaced carbon steel in the fabrication of fuselage tubing, engine mounts, landing gears, and other structural parts. For example, a heat-treated SAE X4130 tube is approximately four times as strong as an SAW 1025 tube of the same weight and size.

A series of chrome-molybdenum steel most used in aircraft construction contains 0.25 to 0.55 percent carbon, 0.15 to 0.25 percent molybdenum, and 0.50 to 1.10 percent chromium. These steels, when suitably heat treated, are deep hardening, easily machined, readily welded by either gas or electric methods, and are especially adapted to high-temperature service.

Inconel is a nickel-chromium-iron alloy closely resembling stainless steel in appearance. Because these two metals look very much alike, a distinguishing test is often necessary. One method of identification is to use a solution of 10 grams of cupric chloride in 100 cubic centimeters of hydrochloric acid. With a medicine dropper, place 1 drop of the solution on a sample of each metal to be tested and allow it to remain for 2 minutes. At the end of this period, slowly add 3 or 4 drops of water to the solution on the metal samples, 1 drop at a time; then wash the samples in clear water and dry them. If the metal is stainless steel, the copper in the cupric chloride solution will be deposited on the metal leaving a copper-colored spot. If the sample is inconel, a new-looking spot will be present.

The tensile strength of inconel is 100,000 psi annealed, and 125,000 psi, when hard rolled. It is highly resistant to salt water and is able to withstand temperatures as high as 1,600°F. Inconel welds readily and has working qualities quite similar to those of corrosion-resistant steels.

Heat Treatment of Ferrous Metals

The first important consideration in the heat treatment of a steel part is to know its chemical composition. This, in turn, determines its upper critical point. When the upper critical point is known, the next consideration is the rate of heating and cooling to be used. Carrying out these operations involves the use of uniform heating furnaces, proper temperature controls, and suitable quenching mediums.

Heat treating requires special techniques and equipment that are usually associated with manufacturers or large repair stations. Because these processes are normally beyond the scope of the field mechanic, the heat treatment of steel alloys will not be discussed. However, the heat treatment of alloy steels includes, hardening, tempering, annealing, normalizing, casehardening, carburizing, and nitriding.

3

Drilling and Countersinking

Although drilling holes seems a simple task, it requires a great deal of knowledge and skill to do it properly and in accordance with specifications. It is one of the most important operations performed by riveters or mechanics. With enough study and a considerable amount of practice, practically anyone can learn to perform the operation.

THE HOLE TRUTH

Preparing holes to specifications requires more than just running a drill through a piece of metal. This chapter outlines the fundamentals of preparing proper holes, primarily for all types of rivets and rivet-type fasteners; however, the information is also generally applicable to bolts, pins, or any other devices that require accurately drilled holes.

Countersinking is another phase of preparing holes for certain types of fasteners. Countersinking procedures and other related data are also included in this chapter.

Rivet Hole Location

Before drilling any hole it is necessary to know where to drill it. This can be done by any one or a combination of the following methods:

- By pilot holes punched while the part is being made on a punch press and enlarging the holes to full size on assembly.
- By use of a template.
- By drilling through drill bushings in a jig on assembly.
- By using a ''hole finder'' to locate holes in the outer skin over the pilot or predrilled hole in the substructure.

• By laying out the rivet pattern by measurements from a blueprint. When it is necessary to mark hole locations, a soft lead pencil should be used. Never use a scriber or other similar object that would scratch the metal.

Drills

Rivet holes are generally made with an air drill motor and a standard straight shank twist drill as shown in Fig. 3-1.

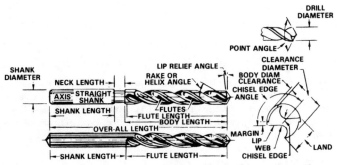

Fig. 3-1. Standard straight shank twist drill.

Drills are made from the following materials:

Carbon Steel. Not normally used in the aerospace industry because of inferior working qualities to high speed steel.

High Speed Steel. Most drills used in the aerospace industry are high speed steel because of good physical characteristics, ready availability, and because they do not present any difficult problems in resharpening.

Cobalt Alloy Steels. Used on high heat treat steels over 180,000 psi.

Cemented Carbide Inserts. Used for cutting very hard and abrasive materials. Limited use in the aerospace industry.

Twist drills for most aircraft work come in three different size groups: "letter" sizes A through Z; "number" sizes 80 through 1; and "fractional" sizes from diameters of $1/64''$ up to $1 1/4''$, increasing in increments of $1/64''$. "Fractional" sizes are also available in larger diameters but are not used for rivet fasteners. All drill sizes are marked on the drill shank. See Fig. 3-2 for normally available drill sizes.

Drill sizes are not always readable on the drill shank because the drill chuck has spun on the drill and removed the markings. If the drill size cannot easily be read on the drill, always use a *drill gauge*, shown in Fig. 3-3.

Drill No.	Frac.	Deci.	Drill No.	Frac.	Deci.	Drill No.	Frac.	Deci.	Drill No.	Frac.	Deci.
80	—	.0135	42	—	.0935	7	—	.201	X	—	.397
79	—	.0145	—	3/32	.0938	—	13/64	.203	Y	—	.404
—	1/64	.0156	41	—	.0960	6	—	.204	—	13/32	.406
78	—	.0160	40	—	.0980	5	—	.206	Z	—	.413
77	—	.0180	39	—	.0995	4	—	.209	—	27/64	.422
76	—	.0200	38	—	.1015	3	—	.213	—	7/16	.438
75	—	.0210	37	—	.1040	—	7/32	.219	—	29/64	.453
74	—	.0225	36	—	.1065	2	—	.221	—	15/32	.469
73	—	.0240	—	7/64	.1094	1	—	.228	—	31/64	.484
72	—	.0250	35	—	.1100	A	—	.234	—	1/2	.500
71	—	.0260	34	—	.1110	—	15/64	.234	—	33/64	.516
70	—	.0280	33	—	.1130	B	—	.238	—	17/32	.531
69	—	.0292	32	—	.116	C	—	.242	—	35/64	.547
68	—	.0310	31	—	.120	D	—	.246	—	9/16	.562
—	1/32	.0313	—	1/8	.125	—	1/4	.250	—	37/64	.578
67	—	.0320	30	—	.129	E	—	.250	—	19/32	.594
66	—	.0330	29	—	.136	F	—	.257	—	39/64	.609
65	—	.0350	—	9/64	.140	G	—	.261	—	5/8	.625
64	—	.0360	28	—	.141	—	17/64	.266	—	41/64	.641
63	—	.0370	27	—	.144	H	—	.266	—	21/32	.656
62	—	.0380	26	—	.147	I	—	.272	—	43/64	.672
61	—	.0390	25	—	.150	J	—	.277	—	11/16	.688
60	—	.0400	24	—	.152	—	9/32	.281	—	45/64	.703
59	—	.0410	23	—	.154	K	—	.281	—	23/32	.719
58	—	.0420	—	5/32	.156	L	—	.290	—	47/64	.734
57	—	.0430	22	—	.157	M	—	.295	—	3/4	.750
56	—	.0465	21	—	.159	—	19/64	.297	—	49/64	.766
—	3/64	.0469	20	—	.161	N	—	.302	—	25/32	.781
55	—	.0520	19	—	.166	—	5/16	.313	—	51/64	.797
54	—	.0550	18	—	.170	O	—	.316	—	13/16	.813
53	—	.0595	—	11/64	.172	P	—	.323	—	53/64	.828
—	1/16	.0625	17	—	.173	—	21/64	.328	—	27/32	.844
52	—	.0635	16	—	.177	Q	—	.332	—	55/64	.859
51	—	.0670	15	—	.180	R	—	.339	—	7/8	.875
50	—	.0700	14	—	.182	—	11/32	.344	—	57/64	.891
49	—	.0730	13	—	.185	S	—	.348	—	29/32	.906
48	—	.0760	—	3/16	.188	T	—	.358	—	59/64	.922
—	5/64	.0781	12	—	.189	—	23/64	.359	—	15/16	.938
47	—	.0785	11	—	.191	U	—	.368	—	61/64	.953
46	—	.0810	10	—	.194	—	3/8	.375	—	31/32	.969
45	—	.0820	9	—	.196	V	—	.377	—	63/64	.984
44	—	.0860	8	—	.199	W	—	.386	—	1	1.000
43	—	.0890				—	25/64	.391			

Fig. 3-2. Sizes and designations of fraction, number, and letter drills.

Drill Points

Drills are made with a number of different points or are ground to different angles for specific application as shown in Fig. 3-4. Always select the correct shape point for the job. As a general rule, the point angle should be flat or large for hard and tough materials, and sharp or small for soft materials.

Drill Sharpening

The twist drill should be sharpened at the first sign of dullness. Faulty sharpening accounts for most of the difficulty encountered in drilling. Although

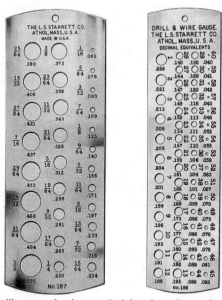

Fig. 3-3. Drill gauges: fractions on the left and number on the right. Decimal equivalents are also given. (Courtesy L.S. Starret Company.)

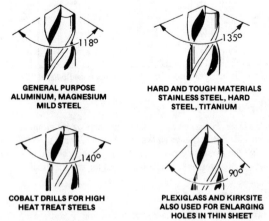

Fig. 3-4. Typical drill points for drilling various materials.

drills can be sharpened by hand, a drill sharpening jig should be used when available. Using the drill gauge (Fig. 3-5), rotating the drill about its central axis will not provide the 12-degree lip clearance required. The drill must be handled such that the heel will be ground lower than the lip. Using the drill gauge, it is possible to maintain equal length lips that form equal angles with the central axis. If the drill is rotated slightly the gauge will indicate whether the heel has sufficient clearance.

Fig. 3-5. Drill sharpening gauge. (Courtesy L.S. Starret Company.)

Drilling Equipment

The *air drill motor* is used in the aerospace industry in preference to an *electric motor* because the air motor has no fire or shock hazards, has a lower initial cost, requires less maintenance, and running speed is easier to control. Air motors are available in a variety of sizes, shapes, running speeds, and drilling head angles (Fig. 3-6).

DRILLING OPERATIONS
Chucking the Drill

WARNING

Before installing or removing drill bits, countersinks, or other devices in an air motor, make sure the air line to the motor is disconnected. Failure to observe this precaution can cause serious injury.

1. Install proper drill in the motor and tighten with proper size chuck key. Be sure to center the drill in the chuck. Do not allow flutes to enter chuck.
2. Connect air hose to motor inlet fitting.
3. Start drill motor and check drill for wobble. Drill must run true, or an oversize hole will be made. Replace bent drills.

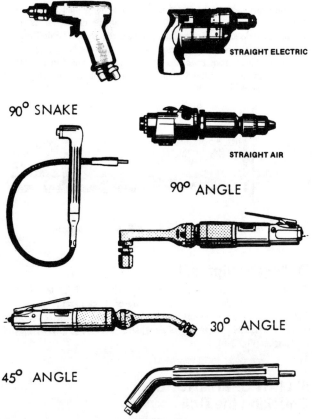

Fig. 3-6. *Typical air motors and attachments.*

Drilling Holes

1. Hold motor firmly. Hold drill at 90-degree angle to the surface as shown in Fig. 3-7.
2. Start hole by placing point of drill on marked centerline. With the fingers, turn the chuck until an indentation is made. (Omit this step when drilling through a drill bushing or when a pilot hole exists.)
3. Position thumb and forefinger to prevent the drill from going too far through the work, which can cause damage to items on the other side or result in an oversize hole.

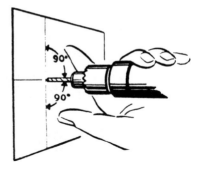

Fig. 3-7. Square drill with work.

4. Drill the hole by starting the drill motor and exerting pressure on centerline of drill. Exert just enough pressure to start the drill cutting a fairly large size chip and maintain this pressure until the drill starts to come through the work.
5. Decrease the pressure and cushion the breakthrough with the fingers when the drill comes through. Do not let the drill go any farther through the hole than is necessary to make a good clean hole. Do not let the drill spin in the hole any longer than necessary.
6. Withdraw drill from hole in a straight line perpendicular to the work. Keep motor running while withdrawing drill.

To ensure proper centering and a correct final size hole, rivet holes are usually pilot drilled with a drill bit that is smaller than the one used to finish the hole. Selected larger diameter holes must be predrilled after pilot drilling and before final size drilling to ensure a round, accurate hole for the rivet. This procedure is sometimes referred to as *step drilling*.

NOTE: When drilling thin sheet metal parts, support the part from the rear with a wooden block or other suitable material to prevent bending.

Using an Extension Drill

Special drills can be used with the air drill motor. The long drill (sometimes called a *flexible drill*) comes in common drill sizes and in 6-inch, 8-inch, 10-inch, or longer lengths. Do not use a longer drill than necessary. See Fig. 3-8.

1. Before starting the motor, hold the extension near the flute end with one hand as shown in Fig. 3-9. Don't touch the flutes and don't forget to wear safety glasses or a face shield.
2. Drill through the part. Do not let go of the drill shank. Keep the motor running as the drill is removed.

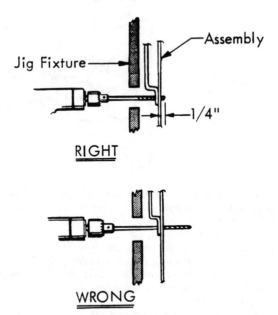

Fig. 3-8. Select a drill of the correct length and size.

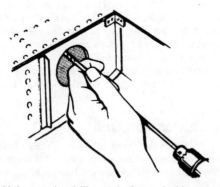

Fig. 3-9. Hold the extension drill near the flute end with one hand. An unsupported drill might whip around and cause injury.

Drilling Aluminum and Aluminum Alloys

Drilling these materials has become quite commonplace and few difficulties are experienced. Some of the newer aluminum alloys of high silicon content and some of the cast alloys still present several problems

General-purpose drills can be used for all sheet material.

High rates of penetration can be used when drilling aluminum; hence disposal of chips or cuttings is very important. To permit these high penetration rates and still dispose of the chips, drills have to be free cutting to reduce the heat generated and have large flute areas for passage of chips.

Although the mechanic has no direct indication of drill motor speed, a relatively high rpm can be used.

Drilling Titanium and Titanium Alloys

Titanium and its alloys have low-volume specific heat and low thermal conductivity, causing them to heat readily at the point of cutting, and making them difficult to cool because the heat does not dissipate readily.

Thermal problems can best be overcome by reducing either the speed or the feed. Fortunately, titanium alloys do not work-harden appreciably, thus lighter feed pressures can be used.

When using super-high-speed drills having high carbon, vanadium, and cobalt to resist abrasion and high drilling heats, a speed (rpm) considerably slower than for aluminum must be used.

Drilling Stainless Steel

Stainless steel is more difficult to drill than aluminum alloys and straight carbon steel because of the work-hardening properties. Because of work-hardening, it is most important to cut continuously with a uniform speed and feed. If the tool is permitted to rub or idle on the work, the surface will become work hardened to a point where it is difficult to restart the cut.

For best results in cutting stainless steel, the following should be adhered to:

- Use sharp drills, point angle 135 degrees.
- Use moderate speeds.
- Use adequate and uniform feeds.
- Use an adequate amount of sulfurized mineral oil or soluble oil as a coolant if possible.
- Use drill motor speeds the same as for titanium.

Hint

When drilling through dissimilar materials, drill through the harder material first to prevent making an egg-shaped hole in the softer material.

Deburring

Drilling operations cause burrs to form on each side of the sheet and between sheets. Removal of these burrs, called *deburring* or *burring*, must be performed if the burrs tend to cause a separation between the parts being riveted. Burrs under either head of a rivet do not, in general, result in unacceptable riveting. The burrs do not have to be removed if the material is to be used immediately; however, sharp burrs must be removed, if the material is to be stored or stacked, to prevent scratching of adjacent parts or injury to personnel.

Care must be taken to limit the amount of metal removed when burrs are removed. Removal of any appreciable amount of material from the edge of the rivet hole will result in a riveted joint of lowered strength. Deburring shall not be performed on predrilled holes that are to be subsequently *form countersunk*.

COUNTERSINKING

Flush head rivets (100 degree countersunk) require a countersunk hole prepared for the manufactured rivet head to nest in. This is accomplished by one of two methods: *machine* countersinking or *form* countersinking (*dimpling*) as shown in Fig. 3-10.

Types of Countersinking Cutters

The *straight shank* cutter is shown in Fig. 3-11. The cutting angle is marked on the body. Cutting angles commonly used are 100-degree and 110-degree. The diameter of the body varies from $1/4''$ to $1^1/2''$. A countersink of $3/8''$ diameter is most commonly used.

A countersink cutter (*rose bud*) for angle drills, also shown in Fig. 3-11, is used if no other countersink will do the job.

The *stop* countersink (Fig. 3-12) consists of cutter and a cage. The cutter has a threaded shank to fit the cage and an integral pilot. The cutting angle is marked on the body. The cage consists of a foot-piece, locking sleeve, locknut, and spindle. The foot-piece is also available in various shapes and sizes. Stop countersinks must be used in all countersinking operations, except where there is not enough clearance.

CAUTION

When using a stop countersink, always hold the skirt firmly with one hand. If the countersink turns or vibrates, the material will be marred and a ring will be made around the hole.

SURFACE COUNTERSUNK

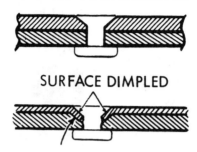

SURFACE DIMPLED

SUB-SURFACE COUNTERSUNK

SURFACE DIMPLED

SUB-SURFACE DIMPLED

Fig. 3-10. Countersinking and dimpling.

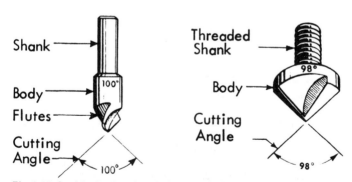

Fig. 3-11. Straight shank and rosebud countersinking cutters.

Back (inverted) countersinks (Fig. 3-13) should be used when access for countersinking is difficult. The back countersink consists of two pieces; a rod, of the same diameter as the drilled hole, which slips through the hole, and a cutter that is attached on the far side.

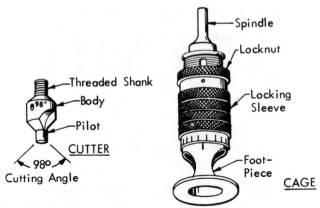

Fig. 3-12. The stop countersink.

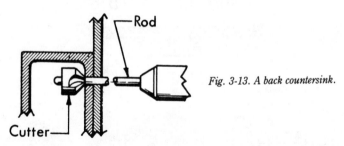

Fig. 3-13. A back countersink.

Countersinking Holes

To countersink holes, proceed as follows:

1. Inspect holes to be countersunk. Holes must be of proper size, perpendicular to work surface, and not elongated.
2. Select proper size countersink. The pilot should just fit the hole and turn freely in the hole. If hole is too tight, the cutter will "freeze-up" in the hole and might break.
3. Check the angle of the countersink.
4. Set the depth of stop countersink on a piece of scrap before countersinking a part. Always check for proper head flushness by driving a few rivets of the required type and size in the scrap material. The rivet heads should be flush after driving. In some cases, where aerodynamic smoothness is a necessity, the blueprint might specify that countersunk

holes be made so that flush head fasteners will be a few thousandths of an inch high. Such fasteners are shaved to close limits after driving.

5. Countersink the part. Be sure to hold the skirt to keep it from marking the part and apply a steady pressure to the motor to keep the cutter from chattering in the hole.

Form Countersinking (Dimpling)

Blueprints often specify form countersinking to form a stronger joint than machine countersinking provides. The sheet is not weakened by cutting metal away, but is formed to interlock with the substructure. The two types of form countersinking accepted are *coin* dimpling and *modified radius* dimpling.

Coin Dimpling

Coin dimpling is accomplished by using either a portable or a stationary squeezer fitted with special dimpling dies (Fig. 3-14). These special dies consist of a male die held in one jaw of the squeezer and a female die held in the other jaw. In the female die, a movable coining ram exerts controlled pressure on the underside of a hole, while the male die exerts controlled pressure on the upper side to form a dimple. Pressure applied by the coining ram forms, or "coins," a dimple in the exact shape of the dies. Coin dimpling does not bend or stretch the material, as did the now obsolete radius dimpling system, and the dimple definition is almost as sharp as that of a machine countersink. Because the lower and upper sides of the dimple are parallel, any number of coined dimples can be nested together or into a machine countersink and the action of the coining ram prevents cracking of the dimple.

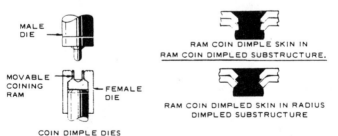

MALE DIE

MOVABLE COINING RAM

FEMALE DIE

RAM COIN DIMPLE SKIN IN RAM COIN DIMPLED SUBSTRUCTURE.

RAM COIN DIMPLED SKIN IN RADIUS DIMPLED SUBSTRUCTURE

COIN DIMPLE DIES

Fig. 3-14. Coin dimple dies and examples of coin dimpling.

Coin dimpling is used on all skins when form countersinking is specified, and, wherever possible, on the substructure. When it is impossible to get coin dimpling equipment into difficult places on the substructure, a modified radius dimple may be used and a coin dimple can then nest in another coin dimple, or a

machine countersink, or a modified radius dimple. Unless the drawing specifies otherwise, dimpling shall be performed only on a single thickness of material.

Modified Radius Dimpling

The modified radius dimple is similar to the coin dimple except the coining ram is stationary in the female die and is located at the bottom of the recess (Fig. 3-15). Because the pressure applied by the stationary coining ram cannot be controlled, the amount of forging, or coining, is limited. The modified radius dimple does not have as sharp a definition as the coin dimple. Because the upper and lower sides of the modified radius dimple are not parallel, this type of dimple can never nest into another dimple or countersink, and when used must always be the bottom dimple. The advantage of the modified radius dimple is that the dimpling equipment can be made smaller and can get into otherwise inaccessible places on the substructure. Dimples for panel fasteners, such as Dzus, Camloc, and Airloc fasteners, might be modified radius dimpled.

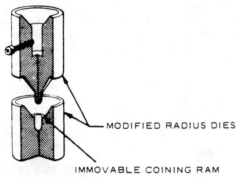

MODIFIED RADIUS DIES

IMMOVABLE COINING RAM

Fig. 3-15. Modified radius dimple dies.

Heat is used with some types of material when doing either type of form dimpling. Magnesium, titanium, and certain aluminum alloys must be dimpled with heated dies. Primed surfaces can be hot or cold dimpled, depending on the metal, and heat can be used to dimple any material, except stainless steel, to prevent cracking. A ram coin hot dimpler is shown in Fig. 3-16.

Hole Preparation for Form Countersinking

Preparation of holes for form countersinking is of great importance because improperly drilled holes result in defective dimples. Holes for solid shank rivets must be size drilled, before dimpling, by using the size drills recommended for regular holes. Holes for other fasteners must be predrilled before

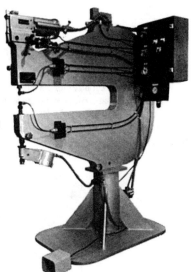

Fig. 3-16. A ram coin hot dimpler.

dimpling, and then drilled to size according to the blueprint or applicable specification after dimpling. Do not burr holes to be form countersunk, except on titanium.

CAUTION

Form countersinking equipment (coin dimpling and modified radius dimpling) is normally operated only by certified operators who have been instructed and certified to operate this equipment.

To accomplish general dimpling, proceed as follows:

1. Fit skin in place on substructure.
2. Pilot drill all holes (Cleco often).
3. Drill to proper size for dimpling: final size for conventional rivets, pre-drill size for all other rivets.
4. Mark all holes according to NAS523 rivet code letters (see chapter 9) to show type and size of fastener *before* removing skin or other parts from assembly. Mark "DD," which means "dimple down," with a grease pencil on head side of the part.
5. Remove skin and have it dimpled.
6. Have substructure dimpled or countersunk as specified on the blueprint. Mark as in step 4.
7. Size drill holes when necessary.

8. Fit skin.
9. Install rivets.

SHAVING FLUSH HEAD FASTENERS

Rivets, bolts, screws, or other fasteners that protrude above the surface (beyond allowable tolerances for aerodynamic smoothness) might require shaving. The amount that a rivet can protrude above the surface of the skin varies with each airplane model and with different surfaces on the airplane. *Rivet shaving (milling)* is accomplished with an air-driven, high-speed cutter in a rivet shaver as shown in Fig. 3-17.

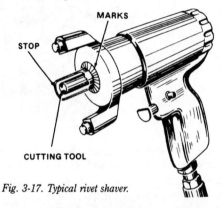

Fig. 3-17. Typical rivet shaver.

After shaving, fasteners, should be flush within .001 inch above the surface, even though a greater protuberance is allowable in that particular area for unshaved fasteners.

WARNING
Shaved fasteners have a sharp edge and could be a hazard to personnel.

Shaved rivets and abraded areas adjacent to shaved rivets and blind rivets that have broken pin ends and are located in parts for which applicable drawings specify paint protection, must be treated for improved paint adhesion.

REAMERS

Reamers are used to smooth and enlarge holes to exact size. Hand reamers have square end shanks so that they can be turned with a tap wrench or similar handle. Various reamers are illustrated in Fig. 3-18.

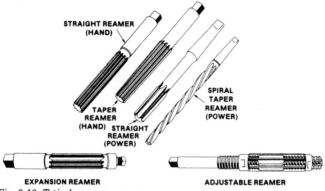

Fig. 3-18. Typical reamers.

A hole that is to be reamed to exact size must be drilled about 0.003- to 0.007-inch undersize. A cut that removes more than 0.007 inch places too much load on the reamer and should not be attempted.

Reamers are made of either carbon tool steel or high-speed steel. The cutting blades of a high-speed steel reamer lose their original keenness sooner than those of a carbon steel reamer; however, after the first superkeenness is gone, they are still serviceable. The high-speed reamer usually lasts much longer than the carbon steel type.

Reamer blades are hardened to the point of being brittle and must be handled carefully to avoid chipping them. When reaming a hole, rotate the reamer in the cutting direction only. Turn the reamer steadily and evenly to prevent chattering, or marking and scoring of the hole walls.

Reamers are available in any standard size. The *straight-fluted* reamer is less expensive than the *spiral-fluted* reamer, but the spiral type has less tendency to chatter. Both types are tapered for a short distance back of the end to aid in starting. *Bottoming* reamers have no taper and are used to complete the reaming of blind holes.

For general use, an *expansion* reamer is the most practical. This type is furnished in standard sizes from $1/4$ to 1 inch, increasing in diameter by $1/32''$ increments.

Taper reamers, both hand- and machine-operated, are used to smooth and true tapered holes and recesses.

4

Riveting

Riveting is the strongest practical means of fastening airplane skins and sub-structure together. Though the cost of installing one rivet is small, the great number of rivets used in airplane manufacture represents a large percentage of the total cost of any airplane.

SOLID-SHANK RIVETS

Although there are many special rivets that are covered later in this chapter, *solid shank* (*conventional*) rivets are the most commonly used rivets in aircraft construction. They consist of a *manufactured head*, a *shank*, and a *driven head*. The *driven head*, sometimes called a *shop* head or *upset* head, is caused by upsetting the shank with a rivet gun or rivet squeezer. The shank actually expands slightly while being driven so the rivet fits tightly in the drilled hole (Fig. 4-1).

Material

Solid shank rivets are manufactured from several kinds of metal or different alloys of these metals to fulfill specific requirements. These different metals and alloys are usually specified in a rivet designation by a system of letters. They are further identified by a system of markings on the rivet head. In some cases the absence of a head marking signifies the alloy within a particular alloy group, or a particular color is used for a particular alloy. Figure 4-2 shows the more commonly used aluminum alloy rivets.

Rivet Types and Identification

In the past, solid shank rivets with several different type heads were manufactured for use on aircraft; now there are only three basic head types used: *countersunk*, *universal*, and *round head*; however, in special cases there are a few exceptions to this rule (Fig. 4-3).

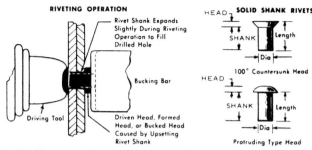

Fig. 4-1. Rivet nomenclature and basic operation.

YOU CAN TELL THE MATERIAL
BY THE HEAD MARKING

Rivet	Material Code	Head Marking	Material
	A	PLAIN (Dyed Red)	1100
	AD	DIMPLED	2117
	DD	TWO RAISED DASHES	2024
	B	RAISED CROSS (Dyed Brown)	5056
	M	TWO DOTS	Monel

Fig. 4-2. Most common aluminum alloy rivets. Many civil and military jet aircraft use 7075 rivets.

Rivets are identified by their MS (Military Standard) number, which superseded the old AN (Army-Navy) number. Both designations are still in use, however (Figs. 4-3 and 4-4).

The 2017-T and 2024-T rivets (Fig. 4-5) are used in aluminum alloy structures where more strength is needed than is obtainable with the same size 2117-T rivet. These rivets are annealed and must be kept refrigerated until they are to be driven. The 2017-T rivet should be driven within approximately

(Continued on page 65.)

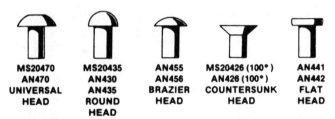

MS20470	MS20435	AN455	MS20426 (100°)	AN441
AN470	AN430	AN456	AN426 (100°)	AN442
UNIVERSAL HEAD	AN435	**BRAZIER HEAD**	**COUNTERSUNK HEAD**	**FLAT HEAD**
	ROUND HEAD			

NOTE: When replacement is necessary for protruding head rivets—roundhead, flathead, or brazier head—they can usually be replaced by universal head rivets.

Fig. 4-3. Style of head and identifying number. The brazier and flat head are obsolete.

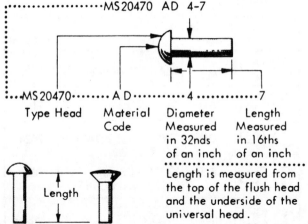

MS20470 AD 4-7

MS20470 .... A D 4 7

| Type Head | Material Code | Diameter Measured in 32nds of an inch | Length Measured in 16ths of an inch |

Length is measured from the top of the flush head and the underside of the universal head.

NOTE: The 2117-T rivet, known as the field rivet is used more than any other for riveting aluminum alloy structures. The field rivet is in wide demand because it is ready for use as received and needs no further heat-treating or annealing. It also has a high resistance to corrosion.

Fig. 4-4. Code breakdown.

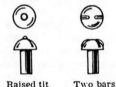

Raised tit   Two bars

Fig. 4-5. "Icebox" rivets: Type D, 2017-T (left) and Type DD, 2024-T (right).

one hour and the 2024-T rivet within 10 to 20 minutes after removal from refrigeration.

The 5056 rivet is used for riveting magnesium alloy structures because of its corrosion-resistant qualities in combinations with magnesium.

Please refer to Fig. 4-5.

These rivets, typed D and DD, require special handling because they are heat treated, quenched, and then placed under refrigeration to delay the age hardening process. The rivets are delivered to the shop as needed and are constantly kept under refrigeration until just before they are driven with a rivet gun or squeezer set.

Remember these points about icebox rivets:

- Take no more than can be driven in 15 minutes.
- Keep rivets cold with dry ice.
- Hit them hard, not often.
- Never put rivets back in refrigerator.
- Put unused rivets in special container provided.

SAFETY PRECAUTION
Dry ice has a temperature of − 105°F. Handle carefully, it can cause a severe burn.

RIVETING PRACTICE
Edge Distance

Edge distance is the distance from the edge of the material to the center of the nearest rivet hole (Fig. 4-6).

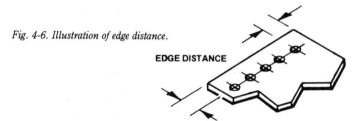

Fig. 4-6. Illustration of edge distance.

If the drawing does not specify a minimum edge distance, the preferred edge distance is double the diameter of the rivet shank (Fig. 4-7).

Rivet Length

Solid shank rivet lengths are never designated on the blueprint; the mechanic must select the proper length (Fig. 4-8).

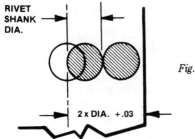

Fig. 4-7. Determining edge distance.

MS20470 & MS20426

The length of the rivet shank extending beyond the material should be 1 1/2 times the diameter of the shank.

Rivet Dia.	Drill Dia.	Upset Dia.		Upset Height	
		Max.	Min.	Max.	Min.
1/16	#51	1/8	5/64	1/16	1/32
3/32	#40	5/32	1/8	1/16	1/32
1/8	#30	7/32	11/64	5/64	3/64
5/32	#21	9/32	13/64	3/32	1/16
3/16	#11	11/32	1/4	1/8	5/64
1/4	6.4MM	27/64	21/64	5/32	3/32
5/16	#0	5/8	13/32	5/16	1/8

Rivet Length = Allowance + Material Thickness

(L = A + MT)

Rivet Diameter	Allowance
1/8	3/16
5/32	1/4
3/16	5/16
1/4	3/8

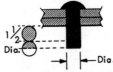

Fig. 4-8. Determining rivet length.

Hole Preparation

Consult chapter 3 for hole preparation details and for information on countersinking of holes and shaving of flush head rivets. Drill sizes for various rivet

diameters is shown in Fig. 4-9. Holes must be clean, round, and of the proper size. Forcing a rivet into a small hole will usually cause a burr to form under the rivet head.

TO DRILL A HOLE FOR THIS SIZE RIVET			USE THIS SIZE DRILL
1/16"	○		#51 (.0670)
3/32"	○		#40 (0.0980)
1/8"	○		#30 (0.1285)
5/32"	○		#21 (0.159)
3/16"	○		#11 (0.191)
1/4"	○		6.4 MM (0.252)

Fig. 4-9. Drill sizes for various rivet diameters.

Use of Clecos

A cleco is a spring loaded clamp used to hold parts together for riveting. Special pliers are used to insert clecos into holes (Fig. 4-10).

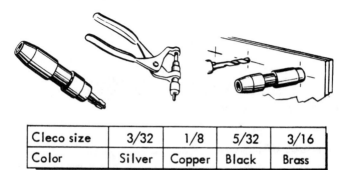

Cleco size	3/32	1/8	5/32	3/16
Color	Silver	Copper	Black	Brass

Fig. 4-10. Clecos are inserted into holes with special cleco pliers. Cleco sizes are identified by colors.

Driving Solid Shank Rivets

Solid rivets can sometimes be driven and bucked by one operator using the conventional gun and bucking bar method when there is easy access to both sides of the work. In most cases, however, two operators are required to drive conventional solid shank rivets.

Rivet Guns

Rivet guns vary in size, type of handle, number of strokes per minute, provisions for regulating speed, and a few other features; but in general operation they are all basically the same (Fig. 4-11). The mechanic should use a rivet gun size that best suits the size of the rivet being driven. Avoid using too light a rivet gun because the driven head should be upset with the fewest blows possible.

NOTE

Always select a rivet gun size and bucking bar weight that will drive the rivet with as few blows as possible.

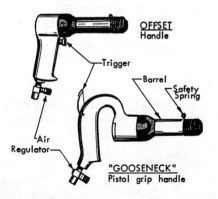

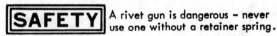

A rivet gun is dangerous – never use one without a retainer spring.

Fig. 4-11. Typical rivet guns.

Rivet Sets

Rivet sets (Fig. 4-12) are steel shafts that are inserted into the barrel of the rivet gun to transfer the vibrating power from the gun to the rivet head (Fig. 4-13).

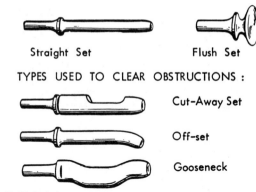

TYPES USED TO CLEAR OBSTRUCTIONS :

Cut-Away Set

Off-set

Gooseneck

Fig. 4-12. Typical rivet sets.

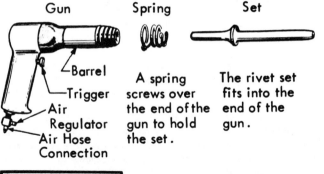

Gun	Spring	Set
Barrel Trigger Air Regulator Air Hose Connection	A spring screws over the end of the gun to hold the set.	The rivet set fits into the end of the gun.

SAFETY A rivet gun is dangerous – never use one without a retainer spring.

Fig. 4-13. The rivet gun and the set go together like this.

Select a rivet set for the style of head and size of rivet. Universal rivet sets can be identified with tool number and size of rivet. Flush sets can be identified only with tool number (Fig. 4-14). Also shown in Fig. 4-14 is the result of using incorrect sets.

Bucking Bars

A bucking bar is a piece of steel used to upset the driven head of the rivet. Bucking bars are made in a variety of sizes and shapes to fit various situations.

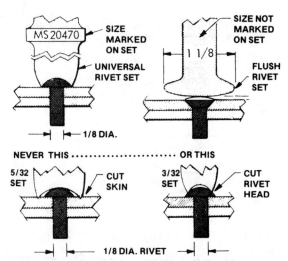

Fig. 4-14. The correct set must be used for the rivet being driven.

Bucking bars must be handled carefully to prevent marring surfaces. When choosing a bucking bar to get into small places, choose one in which the center of gravity falls as near as possible over the rivet shank. Avoid using too light a bucking bar because this causes excessive deflection of the material being riveted that, in turn, might cause marking of the outer skin by the rivet set. A bucking bar that is too heavy will cause a flattened driven head and might cause a loose manufactured head. Remember, you should use as heavy a bar as possible to drive the rivet with as few blows as possible. Figure 4-15 shows some typical bucking bar shapes.

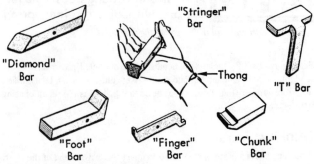

Fig. 4-15. Some typical bucking bars.

Riveting Procedure

Operate a rivet gun and install rivets as follows:

1. Install proper rivet set in gun and attach rivet set retaining spring, if possible. Certain flush sets have no provision for a retaining spring.
2. Connect air hose to gun.
3. Adjust air regulator (Fig. 4-16), which controls the pressure or hitting power of the rivet gun, by holding the rivet set against a block of wood while pulling the trigger, which controls the operating time of the gun. The operator should time the gun to form the head in one "burst," if possible.
4. Insert proper rivet in hole.
5. Hold or wait for bucker to hold bucking bar on shank of rivet. The gun operator should "feel" the pressure being applied by the bucker and try to equalize this pressure.
6. Pull gun trigger to release a short burst of blows. The rivet should now be properly driven, if the timing was correct, and provided the bucking bar and gun were held firmly and perpendicular (square) with the work (Fig. 4-17).

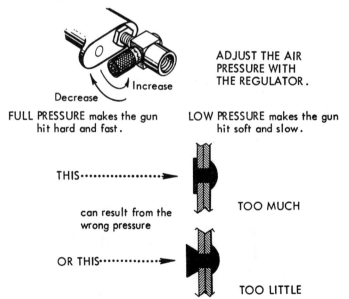

ADJUST THE AIR
PRESSURE WITH
THE REGULATOR.

Decrease Increase

FULL PRESSURE makes the gun
hit hard and fast.

LOW PRESSURE makes the gun
hit soft and slow.

THIS·················➤

can result from the
wrong pressure

TOO MUCH

OR THIS·············➤

TOO LITTLE

Fig. 4-16. Adjust the air regulator that controls the hitting power of the gun by holding the rivet set against a block of wood.

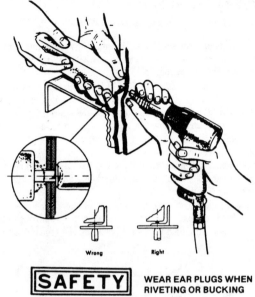

Fig. 4-17. Holding rivet gun and bucking bar on rivet.

Rivet gun operators should always be familiar with the type of structure beneath the skin being riveted and must realize the problems of the bucker (Fig. 4-18).

CAUTION
Never operate a rivet gun on a rivet unless it is being bucked. The bucker should always wait for the gun operator to stop before getting off a rivet.

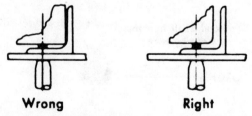

Wrong   **Right**

Fig. 4-18. The bucker should not let the sharp corner of a bucking bar contact an inside radius of the skin or any other object.

Skilled riveters . . .

- Use a slow action gun; it's easier to control.
- Use $1^1/8$-inch bell-type rivet set for general-purpose flush riveting.
- Adjust air pressure sufficiently to drive a rivet in 2 or 3 seconds.
- Use body weight to hold the rivet gun and set firmly against the rivet.
- Hold gun barrel at a 90-degree angle to the material.
- Squeeze trigger by gripping with entire hand as though squeezing a sponge rubber ball. Be sure the bucking bar is on the rivet.
- Operate the rivet gun with one hand; handle rivets with the other hand.
- Spot rivet assembly; avoid reaming holes for spot rivets.
- Plan a sequence for riveting the assembly.
- Drive rivets to a rhythm.

Blind Bucking

In many places on an airplane structure, riveting is visually limited. A long bucking bar might have to be used and, in some cases, the bucker will not be able to see the end of the rivet. Much skill is required to do this kind of bucking in order to hold the bucking bar square with the rivet and to prevent it coming into contact with the substructure. The driven head might have to be inspected by means of a mirror, as shown in Fig. 4-19.

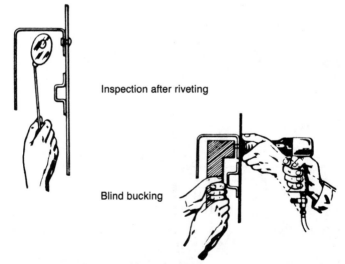

Inspection after riveting

Blind bucking

Fig. 4-19. Blind bucking and inspection.

Tapping Code

A tapping code (Fig. 4-20), has been established to enable the rivet bucker to communicate with the mechanic driving the rivet:

1. One tap on rivet by rivet bucker means start or resume driving rivet.
2. Two taps on rivet by rivet bucker means rivet is satisfactory.
3. Three taps on rivet by rivet bucker means rivet is unsatisfactory and must be removed.

CAUTION

Always tap on the rivet; do not tap on the skin or any part of the aircraft structure.

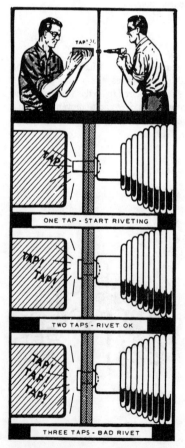

Fig. 4-20. Tapping code.

HAND RIVETING

Hand riveting might be necessary in some cases. It is accomplished by holding a bucking bar against the rivet head, using a draw tool and a hammer to bring the sheets together, and a hand set and hammer to form the driven head (Fig. 4-21). For protruding head rivets, the bucking bar should have a cup the same size and shape as the rivet head. The hand set may be short or long as required. Do not hammer directly on the rivet shank.

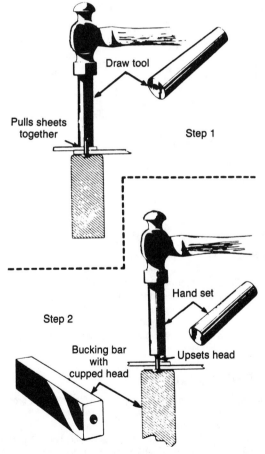

Fig. 4-21. Hand riveting procedure.

RIVET SQUEEZERS

Solid shank rivets can also be driven by using either a portable or stationary rivet squeezer (Fig. 4-22). Both the stationary and portable squeezers are operated by air pressure.

On some stationary squeezers, the rivets are automatically fed to the rivet sets so that the riveting operation is speeded up; on other types, the machines will punch the holes and drive the rivets as fast as the operation permits.

WARNING

Always disconnect the air hose before changing sets in a rivet squeezer.

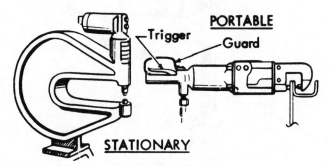

Fig. 4-22. Stationary and portable rivet squeezers.

Inspection after Riveting

Manufactured heads should be smooth, free of tool marks, and have no gap under the head after riveting. There should be no cracks in the skin around the rivet head. The driven head should not be cocked or cracked. The height of the bucked head should be 0.5 times the rivet diameter and the width should be 1.5 times the rivet diameter. There are a few minor exceptions to these rules, but the mechanic should strive to make all rivets perfect. Figure 4-23 illustrates examples of good and bad riveting. For dimensions and tolerances of the upset diameter and height see Fig. 4-8.

RIVET REMOVAL

Solid shank rivet removal is accomplished by the following procedures:

1. Drill through center of rivet head perpendicular to surface of material. Use same drill size as used to make original hole. Drill to the depth where the head of the rivet joins the rivet shank.

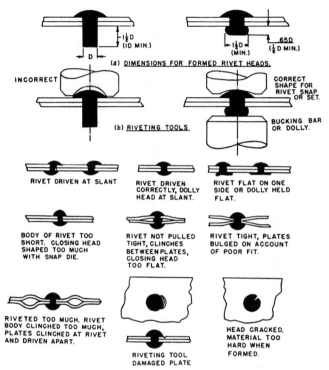

Fig. 4-23. Typical rivet imperfections.

2. Insert drift pin into hole and pry off rivet head. Drift pin shall be same size as drill used to make original hole.
3. Support material from rear with a wooden block and tap out rivet shank with drift pin and lightweight hammer.
4. Install a new rivet, of same type and size as the original, if the hole has not been enlarged in the removal process.
5. If hole has been enlarged or elongated beyond tolerances, the next larger size rivet will have to be used or the part must be scrapped; depending upon the type, size, and location of the rivet.

BLIND RIVETS

There are many places on an aircraft where access to both sides of a riveted structure or structural part is impossible, or where limited space will not permit the use of a bucking bar.

Blind rivets are rivets designed to be installed from one side of the work where access to the opposite side cannot be made to install conventional rivets. While this was the basic reason for the development of blind rivets, they are sometimes used in applications that are not blind. This is done to save time, money, man-hours, and weight in the attachment of many nonstructural parts, such as aircraft interior furnishings, flooring, deicing boots, and the like, where the full strength of solid shank rivets is not necessary. These rivets are produced by several manufacturers and have unique characteristics that require special installation tools, special installation procedures, and special removal procedures.

Basically, nearly all blind rivets depend upon the principle of drawing a stem or mandrel through a sleeve to accomplish the forming of the bucked (upset) head.

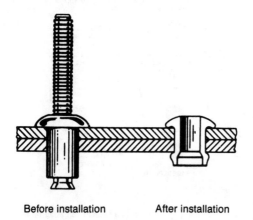

Before installation   After installation

Fig. 4-24. Pull-through rivets (hollow).

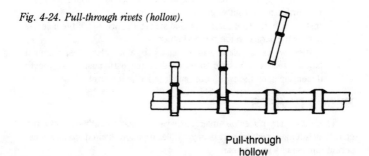

Pull-through
hollow

Although many variations of blind rivets exist, depending on the manufacturer, there are essentially three types:

- Hollow, pull-through rivets (Fig. 4-24), used mainly for nonstructural applications.
- Self-plugging, friction lock rivets (Fig. 4-25), whereby the stem is retained in the rivet by friction. Although strength of these rivets approaches that of conventional solid shank rivets, there is no positive mechanical lock to retain the stem.
- Mechanical locked stem self-plugging rivets (Fig. 4-26), whereby a locking collar mechanically retains the stem in the rivet. This positive lock resists vibration that could cause the friction lock rivets to loosen and possibly fall out. Self-plugging mechanical lock rivets display all the strength characteristics of solid shank rivets and in almost all cases can be substituted rivet for rivet.

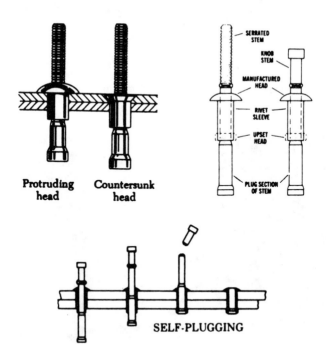

Fig. 4-25. Self-plugging (friction lock) rivets. Two different types of pulling heads are available for friction lock rivets.

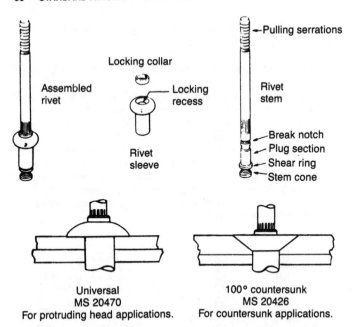

Fig. 4-26. The bulbed Cherrylock rivet includes a locking collar to firmly retain the portion of the stem in the rivet sleeve.

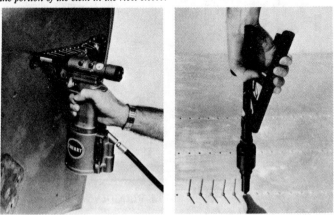

Fig. 4-27. Typical pneumatic and hand-operated pull guns for installation of blind rivets.

Mechanical Locked Stem Self-Plugging Rivets. Mechanical locked stem self-plugging rivets are manufactured by Olympic, Huck, and Cherry Fasteners. The bulbed Cherrylock® (Fig. 4-26) is used as an example of a typical blind rivet that is virtually interchangeable, structurally, with solid rivets.

The installation of all mechanical locked stem self-plugging rivets requires *hand* or *pneumatic pull guns* with appropriate *pulling heads.* Many types are available from the rivet manufacturers; examples of hand and pneumatic-operated pull guns are shown in Fig. 4-27.

The sequence of events in forming the bulbed Cherrylock rivet is shown in Fig. 4-28.

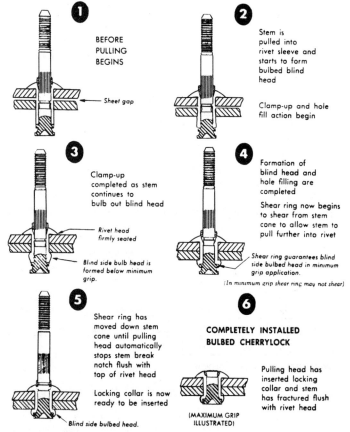

1 BEFORE PULLING BEGINS

Sheet gap

2 Stem is pulled into rivet sleeve and starts to form bulbed blind head

Clamp-up and hole fill action begin

3 Clamp-up completed as stem continues to bulb out blind head

Rivet head firmly seated

Blind side bulb head is formed below minimum grip.

4 Formation of blind head and hole filling are completed

Shear ring now begins to shear from stem cone to allow stem to pull further into rivet

Shear ring guarantees blind side bulbed head in minimum grip application.

(In minimum grip shear ring may not shear)

5 Shear ring has moved down stem cone until pulling head automatically stops stem break notch flush with top of rivet head

Locking collar is now ready to be inserted

Blind side bulbed head.

6 COMPLETELY INSTALLED BULBED CHERRYLOCK

Pulling head has inserted locking collar and stem has fractured flush with rivet head

(MAXIMUM GRIP ILLUSTRATED)

Fig. 4-28. Steps in the formation of the bulbed Cherrylock rivet.

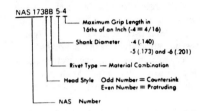

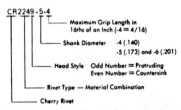

Fig. 4-29. The bulbed Cherrylock rivet numbering system. Note the three diameters available. The bulbed Cherrylock rivet sleeve is 1/64 inch over nominal size. For example, the -4 rivet is a nominal 1/8-inch rivet; however, its diameter is 1/64 inch greater.

Identification of Bulbed Cherrylock Rivets. Figure 4-29 illustrates the numbering system for bulbed Cherrylock rivets.

Hole Preparation. The bulbed Cherrylock rivets are designed to function within a specified hole size range and countersink dimensions as listed in Fig. 4-30.

BULBED CHERRYLOCK

Rivet Diam.	Drill Size	Minimum	Maximum
1/8	#27	.143	.146
5/32	#16	.176	.180
3/16	#5	.205	.209

Do not deburr blind side of hole.

COUNTERSINKING DIMENSIONS

Rivet Diam.	100° MS20426 HEAD		100° NAS1097 HEAD	
	C Max.	C Min.	C Max.	C Min.
3/32	.182	.176	—	—
1/8	.228	.222	.195	.189
5/32	.289	.283	.246	.240
3/16	.356	.350	.302	.296
1/4	.479	.473	.395	.389

Fig. 4-30. Recommended drill sizes, hole size, and countersunk diameter limits.

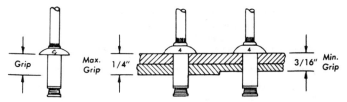

Fig. 4-31. Illustration of grip length.

Grip Length. Grip length refers to the maximum total sheet thickness to be riveted, and is measured in 16ths of an inch. This is identified by the second dash number. All Cherrylock rivets have their grip length (maximum grip) marked on the rivet head, and have a total grip range of $1/16$ of an inch (Example: -4 grip rivet has a grip range of .188″ to .250″) (Fig. 4-31). To determine the proper grip rivet to use, measure the material thickness with a Cherry selector gauge as shown in Fig. 4-32. Always read to the next higher number. To find the rivet grip number without using a selector gauge, determine the total thickness of the material to be fastened; locate between minimum and maximum columns on material thickness chart (Fig. 4-33). Read directly across to right to find grip number.

Further data on bulbed Cherrylock rivets, including materials available, is included in chapter 10, Standard Parts.

Complete installation manuals and pulling tool catalogs are available from the rivet manufacturers.

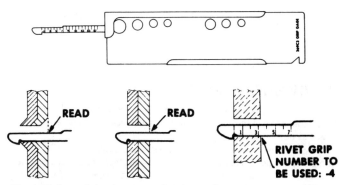

Fig. 4-32. Determining the proper grip using a selector gauge.

MATERIAL THICKNESS RANGE		RIVET GRIP NO.
MINIMUM	MAXIMUM	
See Stds. Pages	1/16"	1
See Stds. Pages	1/8"	2
1/8"	3/16"	3
3/16"	1/4"	4
1/4"	5/16"	5
5/16"	3/8"	6
3/8"	7/16"	7
7/16"	1/2"	8
1/2"	9/16"	9
9/16"	5/8"	10
5/8"	11/16"	11
11/16"	3/4"	12
3/4"	13/16"	13
13/16"	7/8"	14
7/8"	15/16"	15
15/16"	1"	16

Note: For double dimpled sheets, add countersunk rivet head height to material thickness }

CSK BULBED CHERRYLOCK RIVET HEAD HEIGHT	
1/8	.035
5/32	.047
3/16	.063

Fig. 4-33. Determination of rivet grip length without a selector gauge.

PIN (HI-SHEAR) RIVETS

Pin rivets are commonly called Hi-Shear rivets, although "Hi-Shear" is actually the name of the Hi-Shear Corporation, which manufactures pin rivets as well as other products.

Hi-Shear rivets were designed primarily to replace bolts in high-shear strength applications. They are probably the oldest type of high-strength rivet-type fastener used in the aircraft industry. High strength, ease and speed of installation, and weight savings over bolt and nut combinations make them attractive from a design standpoint.

Most Hi-Shear pins are made of heat-treated alloy steel. Some pins, however, are 7075-T6 aluminum alloy, stainless steel or titanium. Most collars are 2117 or 2024-T4 aluminum alloy. Some are mild steel, stainless steel, or monel (Fig. 4-34). The table in chapter 10, Standard Parts, provides head markings, part numbers, and other relative data. When driven with a Hi-Shear set, the work is tightly drawn together and the collar is forced into the pin groove, locking the pin securely into the structure, as in Fig. 4-35.

Fig. 4-34. The Hi-Shear rivet, pin and collar.

Fig. 4-35. The Hi-Shear rivet before and after driving.

Fig. 4-36. Typical Hi-Shear structural connection.

Hi-Shear rivets are used where the loads are high and the structure correspondingly thick (Fig. 4-36), whereas rivets are used where the loads are comparatively low and the structure thin. *Hi-Shear rivets will not strengthen a thin structure connection* because the load required to "shear" a Hi-Shear rivet would cause the structural hole to tear in a (load) "bearing" failure.

Hi-Shear rivets are driven with standard rivet guns or squeezers with a Hi-Shear rivet set adapter as shown in Fig. 4-37.

The set forms the collar to the pin and at the same time cuts off and ejects the excess collar material through the discharge port as shown in Fig. 4-38.

How the Hi-Shear Works. See Fig. 4-39.

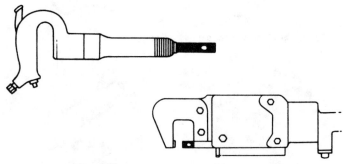

Fig. 4-37. Standard riveting tools with a Hi-Shear rivet set adapter.

Selecting Hi-Shear Rivets. Figure 4-40 shows the Hi-Shear rivet pins available. Additional data is included in chapter 10, Standard Parts.

Part numbers for pin rivets can be interpreted to give the diameter and grip length of the individual rivets. A typical part number breakdown would be as shown in Fig. 4-41.

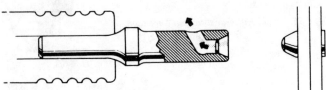

Fig. 4-38. The Hi-Shear rivet set adapter.

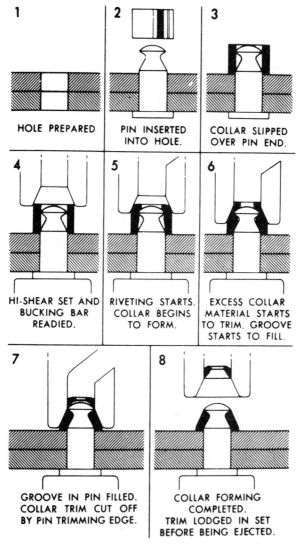

Fig. 4-39. Sequence of events in forming a Hi-Shear riveted joint.

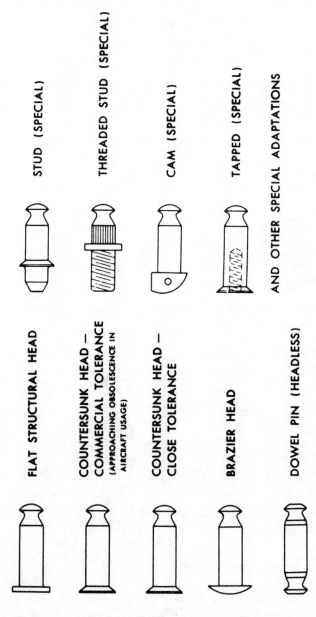

FLAT STRUCTURAL HEAD

COUNTERSUNK HEAD — COMMERCIAL TOLERANCE
(APPROACHING OBSOLESCENCE IN AIRCRAFT USAGE)

COUNTERSUNK HEAD — CLOSE TOLERANCE

BRAZIER HEAD

DOWEL PIN (HEADLESS)

STUD (SPECIAL)

THREADED STUD (SPECIAL)

CAM (SPECIAL)

TAPPED (SPECIAL)

AND OTHER SPECIAL ADAPTATIONS

Fig. 4-40. Various types of Hi-Shear pins. See appendix for further data.

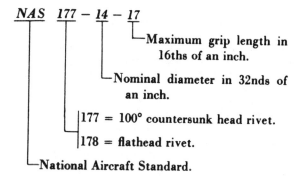

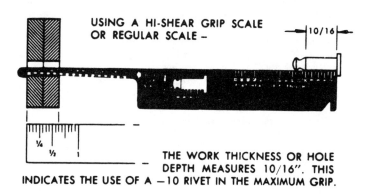

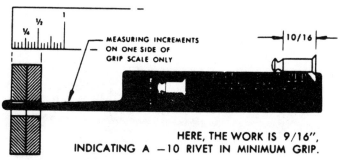

Fig. 4-41. Pin rivet part number designation.

USING A HI-SHEAR GRIP SCALE
OR REGULAR SCALE –

10/16

THE WORK THICKNESS OR HOLE
DEPTH MEASURES 10/16". THIS
INDICATES THE USE OF A –10 RIVET IN THE MAXIMUM GRIP.

MEASURING INCREMENTS
ON ONE SIDE OF
GRIP SCALE ONLY

10/16

HERE, THE WORK IS 9/16",
INDICATING A –10 RIVET IN MINIMUM GRIP.

Fig. 4-42. A grip length scale simplifies determination of rip length.

Determining Grip Length. A special scale is available for determination of grip length (Fig.4-42).

Hole Preparation. Hi-Shear rivets, like bolts, require careful hole preparation. First, the hole must be drilled perpendicular to the manufactured head side of the work. Second, the hole must be sized within proper limits of diameter and roundness. Hi-Shear rivets do not expand during installation; therefore, they must fit the hole into which they are installed.

To obtain accurate holes, machine sharpened drills should be used. Drill motors should have chucks and spindles in good repair. Lubricants should be used on the drill wherever possible. When available, the best precaution of all is to drill through a bushed template or fixture. Where closer tolerances are required, the holes should be reamed. Hole sizes and tolerances are normally specified by engineering and called out on the drawing (blueprint).

NOTE: When countersinking for Hi-Shear rivets, the countersunk hole should not be too deep. When the head is below flush, the head backs up to the bar when it is driven and leaves a gap under the rivet head, resulting in a loose rivet (Fig. 4-43).

Installation. Generally, Hi-Shear riveting is the same as conventional riveting. By changing the standard set to a Hi-Shear set, the rivet gun is ready to shoot Hi-Shear rivets. Typical rivet sets are shown in Fig. 4-44.

The Hi-Shear rivet should be driven quickly. A gun that is heavy enough should be used. The bucking bar should weigh $1^1/3$ times the weight of the gun, or more, for maximum efficiency.

Riveting with Squeezers. Riveting with squeezers is preferred wherever the work permits, as shown in Fig. 4-45.

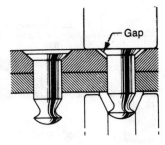

Fig. 4-43. A too-deep countersunk hole results in a loose rivet.

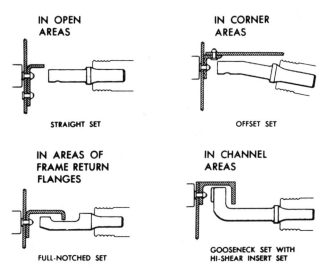

IN OPEN AREAS

STRAIGHT SET

IN CORNER AREAS

OFFSET SET

IN AREAS OF FRAME RETURN FLANGES

FULL-NOTCHED SET

IN CHANNEL AREAS

GOOSENECK SET WITH HI-SHEAR INSERT SET

Fig. 4-44. Hi-Shear rivets are driven with standard rivet guns and bucking bars.

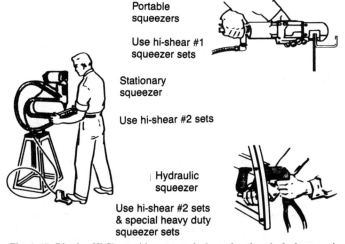

Portable squeezers

Use hi-shear #1 squeezer sets

Stationary squeezer

Use hi-shear #2 sets

Hydraulic squeezer

Use hi-shear #2 sets & special heavy duty squeezer sets

Fig. 4-45. Riveting Hi-Shear with squeezers is the preferred method when practical.

Reverse Riveting. Reverse riveting with Hi-Shear rivets is used where there is no room for a rivet gun (Figs. 4-46 and 4-47). Reverse riveting requires a heavier wallop. The gun should be opened up or a heavier gun should be used.

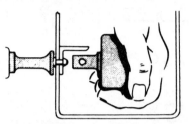

Fig. 4-46. A short straight Hi-Shear set inserted in a Hi-Shear No. 1 or No. 2 bucking bar is used against the collar end. The rivet gun fitted with a flush set supplies the impact to the Hi-Shear head.

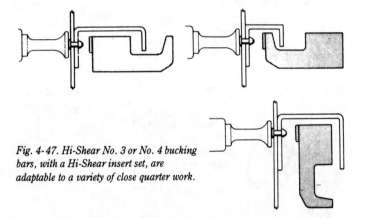

Fig. 4-47. Hi-Shear No. 3 or No. 4 bucking bars, with a Hi-Shear insert set, are adaptable to a variety of close quarter work.

Inspection of Hi-Shear Rivets. If the rivets and collars look good on the outside, they are good on the inside. No gauges or special tools are required.

Hi-Shear Rivet Removal. This method of removal involves using a Hi-Shear rivet cutter to mill off the collar. The pin is removed with punch and hammer as shown in Fig. 4-48. This method, using a cape chisel, is the most commonly used. The collar is split on both sides with a chisel. The pin is removed with a punch and hammer (Fig. 4-49). Another method of Hi-Shear rivet removal is shown in Fig. 4-50.

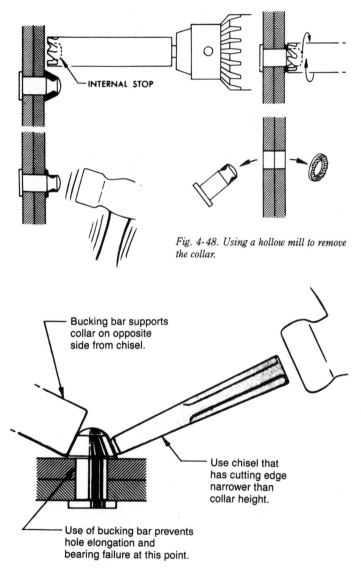

Fig. 4-48. Using a hollow mill to remove the collar.

INTERNAL STOP

Bucking bar supports collar on opposite side from chisel.

Use chisel that has cutting edge narrower than collar height.

Use of bucking bar prevents hole elongation and bearing failure at this point.

Fig. 4-49. The most common collar removal method uses a cape chisel.

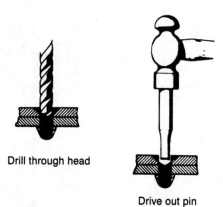

Drill through head

Drive out pin

Fig. 4-50. Drilling out process Hi-Shear rivet removal.

5

Bolts and Threaded Fasteners

Various types of fastening devices allow quick dismantling or replacement of aircraft parts that must be taken apart and put back together at frequent intervals. Bolts and screws are two types of fastening devices that give the required security of attachment and rigidity. Generally, bolts are used where great strength is required, and screws are used where strength is not the deciding factor.

The threaded end of a bolt usually has a nut screwed onto it to complete the assembly. The threaded end of a screw might fit into a female receptacle, or it might fit directly into the material being secured. A bolt has a fairly short threaded section and a comparatively long grip length or unthreaded portion, whereas a screw has a longer threaded section and might have no clearly defined grip length. A bolt assembly is generally tightened by turning the nut on the bolt; the head of the bolt might not be designed for turning. A screw is always tightened by turning its head.

The modern high-performance jet aircraft, however, uses very few "standard" hex head bolts and nuts in its assembly. Also, the "standard" slotted and Phillips head screws are in the minority. Some of these advanced fasteners will be described later in this chapter.

In many cases, a bolt might be indistinguishable from a screw, thus the term "threaded fastener." Also, many threaded fasteners such as the Hi-Lok® and Hi-Lok/Hi Tigue® fasteners are essentially permanent installations like a rivet.

Aircraft threaded fasteners are fabricated from alloy steel, corrosion-resistant (stainless) steel, aluminum alloys and titanium. Most bolts used in aircraft are either alloy steel, cadmium plated, general-purpose AN bolts, NAS close-tolerance, or MS bolts. Aluminum bolts are seldom used in primary structure. In certain cases, aircraft manufacturers make threaded fasteners of different dimensions or greater strength than the standard types. Such

threaded fasteners are made for a particular application, and it is of extreme importance to use like fasteners in replacement.

AIRCRAFT BOLTS

Most, but not all, aircraft bolts are designed and fabricated according to government standards with specifications as follows:

- AN, Air Force/Navy
- NAS, National Aerospace Standards
- MS, Military Standards

See chapter 10, Standard Parts, for a discussion of government standards.

General-Purpose Bolts

The *hex-head* aircraft bolt (AN-3 through AN-20) is an all-purpose structural bolt used for general applications involving tension or shear loads where a light-drive fit is permissible (.006-inch clearance for a $5/8$-inch hole, and other sizes in proportion). They are fabricated from SAE 2330 nickel steel and cadmium plated.

Alloy steel bolts smaller than No. 10-32 ($3/16$-inch diameter, AN-3) and aluminum alloy bolts smaller than $1/4$-inch diameter are not used in primary structures. Aluminum alloy bolts and nuts are not used where they will be repeatedly removed for purposes of maintenance and inspection.

The AN73-AN81 (MS20073-MS20074) drilled-head bolt is similar to the standard hex-bolt, but has a deeper head that is drilled to receive wire for safetying. The AN-3, AN-20 and the AN-73, AN-81 series bolts are interchangeable, for all practical purposes, from the standpoint of tension and shear strengths. (See chapter 10, Standard Parts.)

Identification and Coding

Threaded fasteners are manufactured in many shapes and varieties. A clear-cut method of classification is difficult. Threaded fasteners can be identified by the shape of the head, method of securing, material used in fabrication, or the expected usage. Figure 5-1 shows the basic head styles and wrenching recesses.

AN-type aircraft bolts can be identified by the *code markings* on the boltheads. The markings generally denote the bolt manufacturer, composition of the bolt, and whether the bolt is a standard AN-type or a special purpose bolt. AN standard steel bolts are marked with either a raised dash or asterisk (Fig. 5-2); corrosion-resistant steel is indicated by a single raised dash; and AN aluminum alloy bolts are marked with two raised dashes. Additional information

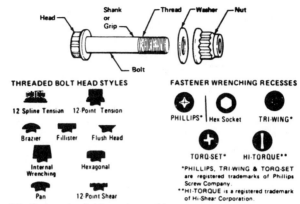

Fig. 5-1. Fastener head styles and wrenching recesses.

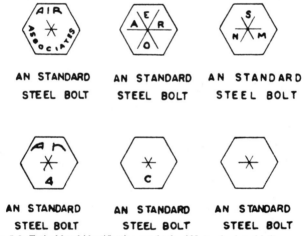

Fig. 5-2. Typical head identification marks for AN standard steel bolts.

such as bolt diameter, bolt length, and grip length can be obtained from the bolt part number. (See chapter 10, Standard Parts.)

AIRCRAFT NUTS

Aircraft nuts are manufactured in a variety of shapes and sizes, made of alloy steel, stainless steel, aluminum alloy, brass, or titanium. No identification

marks or letters appear on nuts. They can be identified only by the characteristic metallic luster or color of the aluminum, brass, or the insert, when the nut is of the self-locking type. They can be further identified by their construction.

Like aircraft bolts, most aircraft nuts are designed and fabricated in accordance with AN, NAS, and MS standards and specifications.

Aircraft nuts can be divided into two general groups: *nonself-locking* and *self-locking* nuts. Nonself-locking nuts (Fig. 5-3) must be safetied by external locking devices, such as cotter pins, safety wire, or locknuts. Self-locking nuts (Figs. 5-4 and 5-5) contain the locking feature as an integral part. Self-locking nuts can be further subdivided into low temperature (250°F or less) and high temperature (more than 250°F).

Most of the familiar nuts—*plain, castle, castellated shear, plain hex, light hex,* and *plain check*—are the nonself-locking type (Fig. 5-3).

The castle nut, AN310, is used with drilled-shank AN hex head bolts, clevis bolts, eyebolts, drilled head bolts, or studs. It is fairly rugged and can withstand large tension loads. Slots (*castellations*) in the nut are designed to accommodate a cotter pin or lock wire for safety. The AN310 castellated, cadmium-plated steel nut is by far the most commonly used airframe nut. (See chapter 10, Standard Parts.)

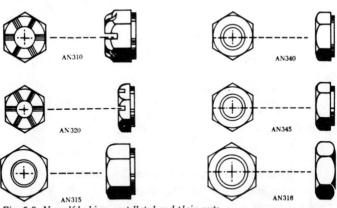

Fig. 5-3. Nonself-locking, castellated and plain nuts.

FLEXLOC® Hex self-locking regular height | Hexagon self-locking castellated nut | 12 point self-locking tension nut | 12 point self-locking shear nut | 12 spline self-locking tension nut | 12 spline self-locking shear nut

Fig. 5-4. High temperature (more than 250°F) self-locking nuts.

Nut

Fiber collar

Fig. 5-5. Low temperature (250°F or less) self-locking nut (elastic stop nut, AN365, MS20365).

The castellated shear nut, AN320, is designed for use with devices (such as drilled clevis bolts and threaded taper pins) that are normally subjected to shearing stress only. Like the castle nut, it is castellated for safetying. Note, however,that the nut is not as deep or as strong as the castle nut; also that the castellations are not as deep as those in the castle nut.

Self-Locking Nuts to 250°F

The *elastic stop* nut is essentially a standard hex nut incorporating a fiber or nylon insert (Fig. 5-5). The inside diameter of the red insert is deliberately smaller than the major diameter of the matching bolt. The nut spins freely on the bolt until the bolt threads enter the locking insert, where they impress, but do not cut, mating threads in the insert. This compression forces a metal-to-metal contact between the top flanks of the nut threads and the bottom flanks of the bolt threads. This friction hold plus the compression hold of the insert essentially ''locks'' the nut anywhere on the bolt.

After the nut has been tightened, the rounded or chamfered end bolts, studs, or screws should extend at least the full round or chamfer through the nut. Flat end bolts, studs, or screws should extend at least $1/32$-inch through the nut. When fiber-type self-locking nuts are reused, the fiber should be carefully checked to make sure it has not lost its locking friction or become brittle. Locknuts should not be reused if they can be run up to a finger-tight position. Bolts $5/16$-inch diameter and larger, with cotter pin holes, can be used with self-locking nuts, but only if free from burrs around the holes. Bolts with damaged threads and rough ends are not acceptable.

Self-locking nuts should not be used at joints that subject either the nut or bolt to rotation. They can be used with antifriction bearings and control pulleys, provided the inner face of the bearing is clamped to the supporting structure by the nut and bolt.

High Temperature Self-Locking Nuts

All-metal locknuts are constructed with either the threads in the locking insert out-of-phase with the load-carrying section (Fig. 5-6), or with a saw-cut

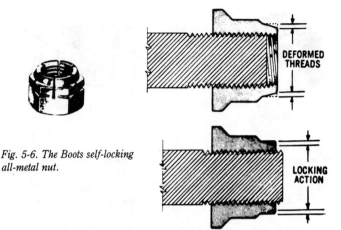

Fig. 5-6. The Boots self-locking all-metal nut.

insert with a pinched-in thread in the locking section. The locking action of the all-metal nut depends upon the resiliency of the metal when the locking section and load-carrying section are engaged by screw threads.

Miscellaneous Nut Types

Self-locking nut bases are made in a number of forms and materials for riveting and welding to aircraft structure or parts (Fig. 5-7). Certain applications require the installation of self-locking nuts in channels, an arrangement that

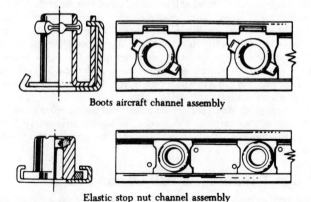

Boots aircraft channel assembly

Elastic stop nut channel assembly

Fig. 5-7. Self-locking nut bases.

permits the attachment of many nuts with only a few rivets. These channels are track-like bases with regularly spaced nuts that are either removable or nonremovable. The removable type carries a floating nut, which can be snapped in or out of the channel, thus making possible the easy removal of damaged nuts. *Clinch* and *spline* nuts, which depend on friction for their anchorage, are not acceptable for use in aircraft structures.

Various types of *anchor* nuts (Fig. 5-8) are available for riveting to structure for application as removable panels.

Fig. 5-8. Examples of anchor nuts.

Sheet spring nuts, sometimes called *speed nuts*, are used with standard and sheet-metal self-tapping screws in nonstructural locations. They find various uses in supporting line clamps, conduit clamps, electrical equipment access doors, and the like, and are available in several types. Speed nuts are made from spring steel and are arched prior to tightening. This arched spring lock prevents the screw from working loose. These nuts should be used only where originally used in fabrication of the aircraft (Fig. 5-9).

Fig. 5-9. Sheet spring nuts are used with self-tapping screws in nonstructural locations.

AIRCRAFT WASHERS

Aircraft washers used in airframe repair are *plain*, *lock*, or *special* washers.

Plain Washers

The plain washer, AN960 (Fig. 5-10), is used under hex nuts. It provides a smooth bearing surface and acts as a shim in obtaining correct grip length for a bolt and nut assembly. It is used to adjust the position of castellated nuts in respect to drilled cotter pin holes in bolts. Plain washers should be used under lock washers to prevent damage to the surface material.

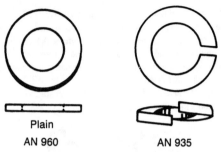

Plain

AN 960   AN 935

Fig. 5-10. Plain and lock washers.

Lock Washers

Lock washers (AN-935 and AN-936) can be used with machine screws or bolts whenever the self-locking or castellated nut is not applicable. They are not to be used as fastenings to primary or secondary structures, or where subject to frequent removal or corrosive conditions.

INSTALLATION OF NUTS AND BOLTS

Boltholes must be normal to the surface involved to provide full bearing surface for the bolthead and nut and must not be oversized or elongated. A bolt in such a hole will carry none of its shear load until parts have yielded or deformed enough to allow the bearing surface of the oversized hole to contact the bolt.

In cases of oversized or elongated holes in critical members, obtain advice from the aircraft or engine manufacturer before drilling or reaming the hole to take the next larger bolt. Usually, such factors as edge distance, clearance, or load factor must be considered. Oversized or elongated holes in noncritical members can usually be drilled or reamed to the next larger size.

Many boltholes, particularly those in primary connecting elements, have close tolerances. Generally, it is permissible to use the first lettered drill size larger than the normal bolt diameter, except where the AN hexagon bolts are used in light-drive fit (reamed) applications and where NAS close-tolerance bolts or AN clevis bolts are used.

Light-drive fits for bolts (specified on the repair drawings as .0015-inch maximum clearance between bolt and hole) are required in places where bolts are used in repair, or where they are placed in the original structure.

The fit of holes and bolts is defined in terms of the friction between bolt and hole when sliding the bolt into place. A *tight-drive fit*, for example, is one in which a sharp blow of a 12- or 14-ounce hammer is required to move the bolt. A bolt that requires a hard blow and sounds tight is considered to fit too tightly. A

light-drive fit is one in which a bolt will move when a hammer handle is held against its head and pressed by the weight of the body.

Examine the markings on the bolthead to determine that each bolt is of the correct material. It is of extreme importance to use like bolts in replacement. In every case, refer to the applicable maintenance instruction manual and illustrated parts breakdown.

Be sure that washers are used under the heads of bolts and nuts unless their omission is specified. A washer guards against mechanical damage to the material being bolted and prevents corrosion of the structural members.

Be certain that the bolt *grip length* is correct. Grip length is the length of the unthreaded portion of the bolt shank (Fig. 5-11). Generally speaking, the grip length should equal the thickness of the materials being bolted together. However, bolts of slightly greater grip length can be used if washers are placed under the nut or the bolthead. In the case of plate nuts, add shims under the plate.

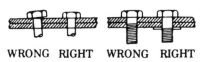

WRONG   RIGHT   WRONG   RIGHT

Fig. 5-11. Bolt installation.

A nut is not run to the bottom of the threads on the bolt. A nut so installed cannot be pulled tight on the structure and probably will be twisted off while being tightened. A washer will keep the nut in the proper position on the bolt.

In the case of self-locking stop nuts, if from one to three threads of the bolt extend through the nut, it is considered satisfactory (Fig. 5-12).

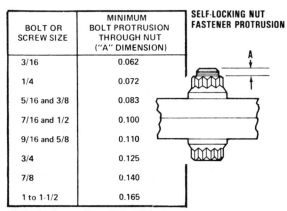

BOLT OR SCREW SIZE	MINIMUM BOLT PROTRUSION THROUGH NUT ("A" DIMENSION)
3/16	0.062
1/4	0.072
5/16 and 3/8	0.083
7/16 and 1/2	0.100
9/16 and 5/8	0.110
3/4	0.125
7/8	0.140
1 to 1-1/2	0.165

Fig. 5-12. Minimum bolt protrusion through nut.

Palnuts (AN356) should be tightened securely but not excessively. Finger-tight plus one to two turns is good practice, two turns being more generally used.

Torque Tables

The standard torque table (Fig. 5-13) should be used as a guide in tightening nuts, studs, bolts, and screws whenever specific torque values are not called out in maintenance procedures.

Cotter Pin Hole Line-Up

When tightening castellated nuts on bolts, the cotter pin holes might not line up with the slots in the nuts for the range of recommended values. Except in cases of highly stressed engine parts, the nut may be over tightened to permit lining up the next slot with the cotter pin hole. The torque loads specified can be used for all unlubricated cadmium-plated steel nuts of the fine or coarse-thread series that have approximately equal number of threads and equal face bearing areas. These values do not apply where special torque requirements are specified in the maintenance manual.

If the head end, rather than the nut, must be turned in the tightening operation, maximum torque values can be increased by an amount equal to shank friction, provided the latter is first measured by a torque wrench.

Safetying of Nuts, Bolts and Screws

It is very important that all bolts or nuts, except the self-locking type, be safetied after installation. This prevents them from loosening in flight due to vibration.

Safety wiring is the most positive and satisfactory method of safetying cap-screws, studs, nuts, boltheads, and turnbuckle barrels that cannot be safetied by any other practical means. It is a method of wiring together two or more units in such a manner that any tendency of one to loosen is counteracted by the tightening of the wire (Fig. 5-14).

COTTER PIN SAFETYING

Cotter pin installation is shown in Fig. 5-14. Castellated nuts are used with bolts that have been drilled for cotter pins. The cotter pin should fit neatly into the hole, with very little sideplay.

INSTALLATION—
BOLT, WASHER, NUT, COTTER PIN

Use Fig. 5-15 as a guide for matching all components of a bolted assembly.

FINE THREAD SERIES

BOLT SIZE	STANDARD TYPE NUTS (MS20365, AN310, AN315)	SHEAR TYPE NUTS (MS20364, AN320, AN316, AN23 THRU AN31)
	INCH-POUNDS	INCH-POUNDS
10-32	20-25	12-15
1/4-28	50-70	30-40
5/16-24	100-140	60-85
3/8-24	160-190	95-110
7/16-20	450-500	270-300
1/2-20	480-690	290-410
9/16-18	800-1,000	480-600
5/8-18	1,100-1,300	660-740
3/4-16	2,300-2,500	1,300-1,500

COARSE THREAD SERIES

BOLT SIZE	STANDARD TYPE NUTS (MS20365, AN310, AN315)	SHEAR TYPE NUTS (MS20364, AN320, AN316, AN23 THRU AN31)
	INCH-POUNDS	INCH-POUNDS
8-32	12-15	7-9
10-24	20-25	12-15
1/4-20	40-50	25-30
5/16-18	80-90	48-55
3/8-16	160-185	95-110
7/16-14	235-255	140-155
1/2-13	400-480	240-290
9/16-12	500-700	300-420
5/8-11	700-900	420-540
3/4-10	1,150-1,600	700-950

Fig. 5-13. Standard torque tables.

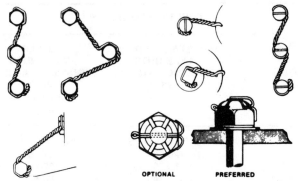

Fig. 5-14. Typical safety wiring methods.

BOLT		WASHER	NUT	COTTER PIN	
AN	DIAM.-THRD.	AN	AN	AN	DIAM.
– 3	(³/₁₆) 10-32		310-3	380-2	¹/₁₆
– 3A		960-10	365-1032	None	
4	¹/₄-28		310-4	380-2	¹/₁₆
4A		960-416	365-428	None	
5	⁵/₁₆-24		310-5	380-2	¹/₁₆
5A		960-516	365-524	None	
6	³/₈-24		310-6	380-3	³/₃₂
6A		960-616	365-624	None	
7	⁷/₁₆-20		310-7	380-3	³/₃₂
7A		960-716	365-720	None	
8	¹/₂-20		310-8	380-3	³/₃₂
8A		960-816	365-820	None	

Fig. 5-15. Guide for installation of bolt, washer, nut, and cotter pin assembly.

MISCELLANEOUS THREADED FASTENERS

As stated earlier in this chapter, standard hex, slotted, and Phillips head threaded fasteners are seldom used for structural applications on high-performance aircraft. For example, most threaded fasteners on the L-1011 jet transport aircraft are ''Tri-Wing'' developed by the Phillips Screw Company. Other

types in general use are ''Torq-Set'' and ''Hi-Torque.'' All of these patented fasteners require special driving bits that fit into standard holders and screwdriver handles.

The Tri-Wing is shown in Fig. 5-16. Other fastener wrenching recesses are shown in Fig. 5-1. Various fasteners are illustrated in chapter 10, Standard Parts.

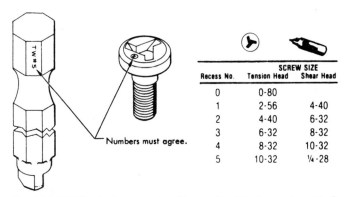

| Recess No. | SCREW SIZE | |
	Tension Head	Shear Head
0	0-80	
1	2-56	4-40
2	4-40	6-32
3	6-32	8-32
4	8-32	10-32
5	10-32	¼-28

Numbers must agree.

Fig. 5-16. Tri-Wing heads are numbered for easy identification, and must be fitted with a like-numbered bit for effective driving.

Machine Screws

Machine screw threads usually run to the head and thus leave no grip for shear bearing. Machine screws, therefore, are used in tension with no concern for the threads extending into the hole.

A number of different head types are available on machine screws to satisfy the particular installation.

For any type of screw there is a correct screwdriver. If the screw has a slotted head, the screwdriver should fit the slot snugly (Fig. 5-17). The sides of the screwdriver should, as nearly as possible, be parallel to the screw slot sides.

Reed and Prince or *Phillips* heads require a special driver made for the particular screw. The drivers for the two are not interchangeable (Fig. 5-18). The Phillips head has rounded shoulders in the recess while the Reed and Prince has sharp square shoulders. The use of the wrong screwdriver on these screws might result in ruining the screw head. The use of power (electric and pneumatic) screwdrivers has speeded up many installations, such as inspection doors and fillets, where the tool might be used in rapid succession on a row of screws.

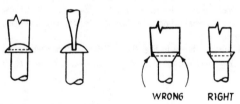

Fig. 5-17. A correct size screwdriver must be used.

PHILLIPS   **REED & PRINCE**

Fig. 5-18. A Phillips screw is different from a Reed & Prince screw.

Instead of a nut, threads are often tapped into the bolted structure. In this case, the bolts or screws are safetied with a wire through a hole drilled in the head (Fig. 5-14). Whenever possible, the wire should be so strong that tension is held on the bolt or screw toward tightening it. Always keep in mind the fact that the wire should tend to tighten the screws.

Machine screws (Fig. 5-19) are usually *flathead* (*countersunk*), *roundhead*, or *washer-head*. These screws are general-purpose screws and are available in the low-carbon steel, brass, corrosion-resistant steel, and aluminum alloy.

Fig. 5-19. Several types of machine screws (also see the appendix).

Roundhead screws, AN515 and AN520, have either slotted or recessed heads. The AN515 screw has coarse threads and the AN520 has fine threads.

Countersunk machine screws are listed as AN505 and AN510 for 82 degrees, and AN507 for 100 degrees. The AN505 and AN510 correspond to the AN515 and AN520 roundhead in material and usage.

The *fillister-head* screw, AN500 through AN503, is a general-purpose screw and is used as a capscrew in light mechanisms. This could include attachments of cast aluminum parts, such as gearbox cover plates.

The AN500 and AN501 screws are available in low-carbon steel, corrosion-resistant steel, and brass. The AN500 has coarse threads while the AN501 has fine threads. They have no clearly defined grip length. Screws larger than No. 6 have a hole drilled through the head for safetying purposes.

The AN502 and AN503 fillister-head screws are made of heat-treated alloy steel, have a small grip, and are available in fine and coarse threads. These screws are used as capscrews where great strength is required. The coarse-threaded screws are commonly used as capscrews in tapped aluminum alloy and magnesium castings because of the softness of the metal.

Dzus Fasteners

Although not a threaded fastener, the Dzus fastener is an example of a quick-disconnect fastener, such as used on a cowling or nacelle.

The Dzus turnlock fastener consists of a stud, grommet, and receptacle. Figure 5-20 illustrates an installed Dzus fastener and the various parts.

The grommet is made of aluminum or aluminum alloy material. It acts as a holding device for the stud. Grommets can be fabricated from 1100 aluminum tubing, if none are available from normal sources.

The spring is made of steel, cadmium-plated to prevent corrosion. The spring supplies the force that locks or secures the stud in place when two assemblies are joined.

The studs are fabricated from steel and are cadmium-plated. They are available in three head styles: wing, flush, and oval.

A quarter of a turn of the stud (clockwise) locks the fastener. The fastener can be unlocked only by turning the stud counterclockwise. A Dzus key, or a specially ground screwdriver, locks or unlocks the fastener.

Special installation tools and instructions are available from the manufacturers.

HI-LOK AND HI-LOK/HI-TIGUE FASTENERS

The patented, high strength Hi-Lok or Hi-Lok/Hi-Tigue originated by the Hi-Shear Corporation is basically a threaded fastener that combines the best features of a rivet and bolt (Fig. 5-21). It consists of two parts, a threaded pin and a threaded collar. The Hi-Tigue fastener is an updated Hi-Lok fastener.

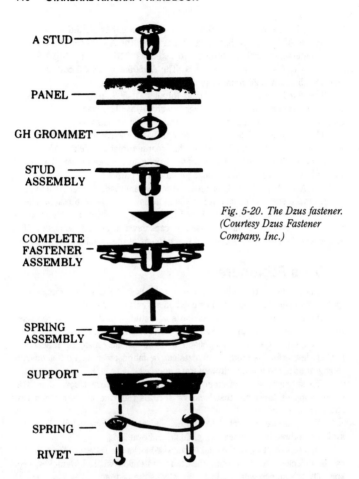

A STUD

PANEL

GH GROMMET

STUD ASSEMBLY

COMPLETE FASTENER ASSEMBLY

SPRING ASSEMBLY

SUPPORT

SPRING

RIVET

Fig. 5-20. The Dzus fastener. (Courtesy Dzus Fastener Company, Inc.)

Three primary design advantages are:

- A controlled preload or clamp-up consistent within ± 10 percent designed into the fastener.
- Minimum size and weight.
- Simple, quiet, and rapid installation, done from one side of the work by one worker.

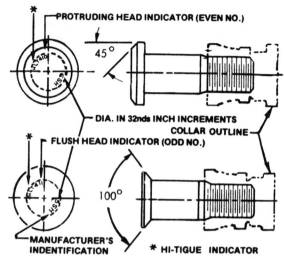

Fig. 5-21. The Hi-Lok, Hi-Lok/Hi-Tigue pin and collar. (Courtesy Hi-Shear Corporation.)

Because of the collar's break-off at the design preload, torque inspection after installation is eliminated, along with the problems of torque wrench use and calibration.

The threaded end of the Hi-Lok pin contains a hexagonal-shaped recess. The hex wrench tip of the Hi-Lok driving tool engages the recess to prevent rotation of the pin while the collar is being installed. The pin recess also offers a secondary benefit, weight savings.

The pin is designed in two basic head styles. For shear applications the pin is made in the lightweight, Hi-Shear countersunk style, and in a compact protruding head style. For tension applications, the MS24694 (AN509) flush and protruding head styles are available.

The self-locking, threaded Hi-Lok collar has an internal counterbore at the base to accommodate variations in material thickness. At the opposite end of the collar is a wrenching device that is torqued by the driving tool until it shears off during installation; this shear-off point occurs when a predetermined preload or clamp-up is attained in the fastener during installation. Removal of the collar wrenching surfaces after installation saves additional weight.

The basic part number indicates the assembly of the pin and the collar part numbers (Fig. 5-22).

See tables in chapter 10, Standard Parts, for representative standard fastener assemblies.

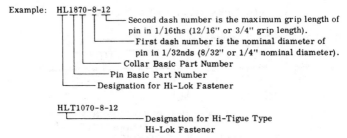

Fig. 5-22. Hi-Lok/Hi-Tigue basic part number. (Courtesy Hi-Shear Corporation.)

The Hi-Lok/Hi-Tigue interference-fit pin provides improved fatigue benefits to the airframe structure. The Hi-Tigue feature on the end of the pin shank makes it possible to use a straight shank interference-fit fastener in a standard straight drilled hole to obtain the maximum fatigue life of the structure.

The Hi-Tigue pin can be considered a combination of a standard precision pin with a slightly oversize precision ball positioned between the threads and the shank of the pin as shown in Fig. 5-23. Figure 5-24 shows the Hi-Tigue bead area in exaggerated views.

STANDARD HI-LOK PIN   PRECISION BALL   HI-LOK/HI-TIGUE PIN
                             (GREATER IN DIAMETER
                             THAN PIN SHANK)

Fig. 5-23. The Hi-Lok/Hi-Tigue fastener concept. (Courtesy Hi-Shear Corporation.)

The Hi-Lok/Hi-Tigue pin is a straight shank, precision, threaded pin featuring a subtly shaped bead at the thread end of the shank (Fig. 5-24). The pin is installed in a straight-walled hole drilled normally at 0.002 to 0.004 inch diametral interference. The pin is available in 70° and 100° flush heads as well as protruding head styles for shear and tension applications. Pins are manufactured from all commonly used fastener alloys, including titaniums, alloy steels, and corrosion resistant steels.

The Hi-Lok/Hi-Tigue collar is identical to the self-locking, standard controlled torque Hi-Lok collar with the exception of the internal counterbore. In the Hi-Tigue version, the counterbore is dimensioned to accommodate the

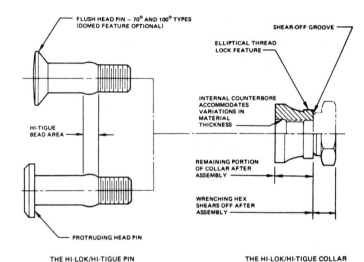

FLUSH HEAD PIN – 70° AND 100° TYPES
(DOMED FEATURE OPTIONAL)

SHEAR-OFF GROOVE

ELLIPTICAL THREAD
LOCK FEATURE

INTERNAL COUNTERBORE
ACCOMMODATES
VARIATIONS IN
MATERIAL
THICKNESS

HI-TIGUE
BEAD AREA

REMAINING PORTION
OF COLLAR AFTER
ASSEMBLY

WRENCHING HEX
SHEARS OFF AFTER
ASSEMBLY

PROTRUDING HEAD PIN

THE HI-LOK/HI-TIGUE PIN

THE HI-LOK/HI-TIGUE COLLAR

Fig. 5-24. The Hi-Lok/Hi-Tigue fastening system. (Courtesy Hi-Shear Corporation.)

pin's Hi-Tigue bead during assembly. Hi-Tigue collars are available for shear, tension, and temperature applications. Collar materials include 2024-T6 aluminum alloy, A-286 alloy, 17-4PH, Type 303 stainless steel, and titanium alloy.

A self-sealing torque-controlled collar containing a Teflon sealing insert within its internal counterbore is available to provide fuel-tight joints without the need for sealants.

During assembly of the collar to the pin, using standard Hi-Lok installation tools, the pin is seated into its final position and the structure pieces are drawn tightly together. Because of the collar's wrenching hex shear-off at design preload, torque inspection after installation is eliminated together with the inherent problems of torque wrench use and calibration. Inspection is visual only; no mechanical torque check is required.

Versatile pneumatic Hi-Lok installation tools assemble both the standard and Hi-Tigue versions of the Hi-Lok fastener. Basic Hi-Lok tooling is available in straight, offset, extended, and 90° right angle types to provide accessibility into a variety of open or congested structures. Automatic collar-driving tools permit assembly of Hi-Loks up to 40 per minute. Tape-controlled automatic machines have been developed to completely automate the installation of Hi-Lok/Hi-Tigues: drill, countersink, select the proper grip length, insert the pin, and drive the collar.

INSTALLATION OF HI-LOK
AND HI-LOK/HI-TIGUE FASTENERS
Hole Preparation

Hi-Lok pins require reamed and chamfered holes and, in some cases, an interference-fit. For standard Hi-Lok pins, it is generally recommended that the maximum interference-fit shall not exceed 0.002 inch. The Hi-Tigue-type Hi-Lok pin is normally installed in a hole at 0.002 to 0.004 inch diametral interference.

The Hi-Lok pin has a slight radius under its head (Fig. 5-25). After drilling, deburr the edge of the hole. This permits the head to fully seat in the hole. See appropriate Hi-Lok standards for head radius dimensions. For example, the $3/16$ protruding head has a .015/.025 radius, while the $3/16$ flush head has a .025/.030 radius.

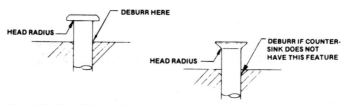

Fig. 5-25. The Hi-Lok and Hi-Lok/Hi-Tigue pins have a slight radius under their heads. (Courtesy Hi-Shear Corporation.)

Pin Grip Length

Standard pin lengths are graduated in $1/16$-inch increments. The material thickness can vary $1/16$ inch without changing pin lengths. Adjustment for variations in material thickness in between the pin $1/16$-inch graduations is automatically made by the counterbore in the collar (Fig. 5-26).

Grip length is determined as shown in Fig. 5-27.

Installation Tools

Hi-Lok fasteners are rapidly installed by one person working from one side of the work using standard power or hand tools and Hi-Lok adaptor tools.

Hi-Lok adaptor tools are fitted to high-speed pistol grip and ratchet wrench drives in straight, 90-degree, offset extension, and automatic collar-feed configurations. Figure 5-28 shows a few of the hand and power tools available for installing Hi-Lok and Hi-Lok/Hi-Tigue fasteners.

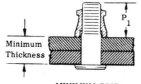

MINIMUM GRIP
(Maximum Protrusion)

MAXIMUM GRIP
(Minimum Protrusion)

Standard Hi-Lok Pin		Minimum Protrusion P	Maximum Protrusion P_1
First Dash Number	Nominal Diameter		
-5	5/32	.302	.384
-6	3/16	.315	.397
-8	1/4	.385	.467
-10	5/16	.490	.572
-12	3/8	.535	.617
-14	7/16	.625	.707
-16	1/2	.675	.757
-18	9/16	.760	.842
-20	5/8	.815	.897
-24	3/4	1.040	1.122
-28	7/8	1.200	1.282
-32	1	1.380	1.462

Fig. 5-26. Table showing installed Hi-Lok Pin protrusion limits. (Courtesy Hi-Shear Corporation.)

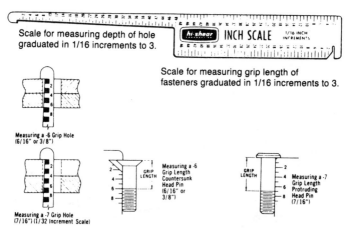

Fig. 5-27. Determining grip length using a special scale. (Courtesy Hi-Shear Corporation.)

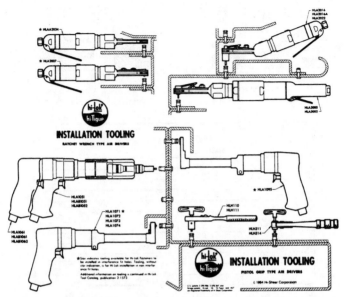

Fig. 5-28. A few of the hand and power tools available for installing Hi-Lok and Hi-Lok/Hi-Tigue fasteners. (Courtesy Hi-Shear Corporation.)

The basic consideration in determining the correct hand tool is to match the socket-hex tip dimensions of the tool with the Hi-Lok/Hi-Tigue pin hex recess and collar driving hex of the particular pin-collar combination to be installed. Figure 5-29 indicates the hex dimensions that must match.

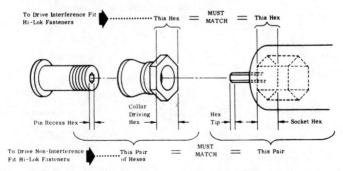

Fig. 5-29. Determining the correct hand tool by matching hex dimensions. (Courtesy Hi-Shear Corporation.)

Installation Steps in Noninterference-Fit Hole

Figure 5-30 shows the installation steps in a noninterference-fit hole.

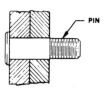

a. Insert the pin into the prepared non-interference fit hole.

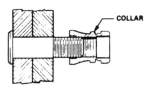

b. Manually thread the collar onto the pin.

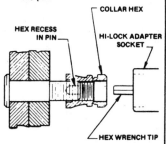

c. Insert the hex wrench tip of the power driver into the pin's hex recess, and the socket over the collar hex. This prevents rotation of the pin while the collar is being installed.

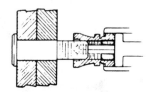

d. Firmly press the power driver against the collar, operate the power driver until the collar's wrenching device has been torqued off.

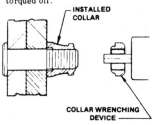

e. This completes the installation of the Hi-Lok Fastener Assembly.

NOTE:

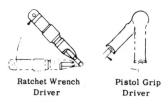

Ratchet Wrench Driver   Pistol Grip Driver

To ease the removal of the driving tool's hex wrench tip from the hex recess of the pin after the collar's wrenching device has sheared off, simply rotate the entire driver tool in a slight clockwise motion.

Fig. 5-30. Installation steps in noninterference fit hole. (Courtesy Hi-Shear Corporation.)

Installation Steps in Interference-Fit Hole

When Hi-Lok/Hi-Tigues are installed in an interference-fit, the pins should be driven in using a standard rivet gun and Hi-Tigue pin driver as shown in Fig. 5-31. The structure must be supported with a draw bar as shown.

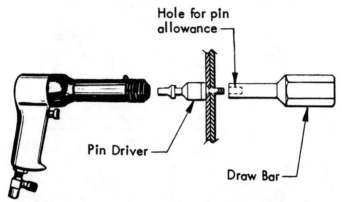

Fig. 5-31. Installing an interference fit Hi-Tigue pin using a rivet gun. (Courtesy Hi-Shear Corporation.)

When Hi-Lok/Hi-Tigue pins are pressed or tapped into holes, the fit is sufficiently tight to grip the pin to prevent it from rotating. Hi-Lok driver tools are available that use a finder pin instead of the hex wrench tip to locate the tool on the collar and pin (Fig. 5-32). Otherwise, installation steps for interference-fit holes are the same as for standard Hi-Lok fasteners.

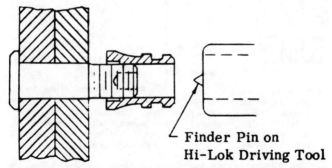

Fig. 5-32. Finder pin on Hi-Lok driving tool. (Courtesy Hi-Shear Corporation.)

For field service, all sizes of Hi-Lok fasteners can be installed with hand tools (standard Allen hex keys and open-end or ratchet type wrenches.)

Inspection after Installation

Hi-Lok and Hi-Lok/Hi-Tigue fasteners are visually inspected. No torque wrenches are required.

The Hi-Lok protrusion gauges offer a convenient method to check Hi-Lok pin protrusion limits after the Hi-Lok pin has been inserted in the hole and before or after collar installation (Fig. 5-33). Individual gauges accommodate Hi-Lok pin diameter sizes $5/32$, $3/16$, $1/4$, $5/16$, and $3/8$. Gauges are made of .012 stainless steel and are assembled as a set on a key chain.

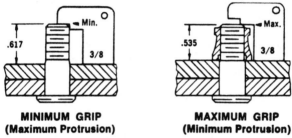

MINIMUM GRIP
(Maximum Protrusion)

MAXIMUM GRIP
(Minimum Protrusion)

Fig. 5-33. Protrusion limits for standard Hi-Lok pins; 3/8 gauge shown as an example. (Courtesy Hi-Shear Corporation.)

Removal of Installed Fastener

Removal of fasteners is accomplished with standard hand tools in a manner similar to removing a nut from a bolt. By holding the pin with a standard Allen wrench, the collar can be removed with pliers. Hollow mill-type cutters attached to power tools can also remove the collars without damage to the pin, and the pins can be reused if undamaged. Special hand and power removal tools are also available.

6

Aircraft Plumbing

FLUID LINES

Aircraft plumbing lines usually are made of metal tubing and fittings or of flexible hose. Metal tubing is widely used in aircraft for fuel, oil, coolant, oxygen, instrument, and hydraulic lines. Flexible hose is generally used with moving parts or where the hose is subject to considerable vibration.

Generally, aluminum alloy or corrosion-resistant steel tubing have replaced copper tubing. The workability, resistance to corrosion, and light weight of aluminum alloy are major factors in its adoption for aircraft plumbing.

In some special high-pressure (3,000 psi) hydraulic installations, corrosion-resistant steel tubing, either annealed or $1/4$-hard, is used. Corrosion-resistant steel tubing does not have to be annealed for flaring or forming; in fact, the flared section is somewhat strengthened by the cold working and strain hardening during the flaring process.

Corrosion resistant steel tubing, annealed $1/4$-hard, is used extensively in high-pressure hydraulic systems for the operation of landing gear, flaps, brakes, and the like. External brake lines should always be made of corrosion-resistant steel to minimize damage from rocks thrown by the tires during takeoff and landing, and from careless ground handling. Although identification markings for steel tubing differ, each usually includes the manufacturer's name or trademark, the SAE number, and the physical condition of the metal.

Aluminum alloy tubing, 1100 ($1/2$-hard) or 3003 ($1/2$-hard), is used for general purpose line of low or negligible fluid pressures, such as instrument lines and ventilating conduits. The 2024-T and 5052-0 aluminum alloy materials are used in general-purpose systems of low and medium pressures, such as hydraulic and pneumatic 1,000 to 1,500 psi systems and fuel and oil lines. Occasionally, these materials are used in high pressure (3,000 psi) systems.

Tubing made from 2024-T and 5052-0 materials will withstand a fairly high pressure before bursting. These materials are easily flared and are soft enough to be formed with hand tools and, therefore, must be handled with care to prevent scratches, dents, and nicks.

Metal tubing is sized by *outside diameter*, which is measured fractionally in sixteenths of an inch. Thus, Number 6 tubing is $^6/_{16}$ (or $^3/_8$-inch) and Number 8 tubing is $^8/_{16}$ ($^1/_2$-inch), and the like.

In addition to other classifications or means of identification, tubing is manufactured with a specific *wall thickness*. Thus, it is important when installing tubing to know not only the material and outside diameter, but also the thickness of the wall.

FLEXIBLE HOSE

Flexible hose is used in aircraft plumbing to connect moving parts with stationary parts in locations subject to vibration or where a great amount of flexibility is needed. It can also serve as a connector in metal tubing systems.

Synthetics

Synthetic materials most commonly used in the manufacture of flexible hose are Buna-N, Neoprene, Butyl, and Teflon (trademark of DuPont Corp.). Buna-N is a synthetic rubber compound that has excellent resistance to petroleum products. Do not confuse with Buna-S. Do not use for phosphate ester base hydraulic fluid (Skydrol®). Neoprene is a synthetic rubber compound that has an acetylene base. Its resistance to petroleum products is not as good as Buna-N, but has better abrasive resistance. Do not use for phosphate ester base hydraulic fluid (Skydrol). Butyl is a synthetic rubber compound made from petroleum raw materials. It is an excellent material to use with phosphate ester based hydraulic fluid (Skydrol). Do not use with petroleum products. Teflon is the DuPont trade name for tetrafluorethylene resin. It has a broad operating temperature range ($-65°F$ to $450°F$). It is compatible with nearly every substance or agent used. It offers little resistance to flow; sticky viscous materials will not adhere to it. It has less volumetric expansion than rubber and the shelf and service life is practically limitless.

Rubber Hose

Flexible rubber hose consists of a seamless synthetic rubber inner tube covered with layers of cotton braid and wire braid, and an outer layer of rubber-impregnated cotton braid. This type of hose is suitable for use in fuel, oil, coolant, and hydraulic systems. The types of hose are normally classified by the amount of pressure they are designed to withstand under normal operating conditions:

- Low pressure; any pressure below 250 psi; fabric braid reinforcement.
- Medium pressure; pressures up to 3,000 psi; one wire braid reinforce-

ment. Smaller sizes carry pressure up to 3,000 psi; larger sizes carry pressure up to 1,000 psi

• High pressure; all sizes up to 3,000 psi operating pressures.

Teflon Hose

Teflon hose is a flexible hose designed to meet the requirements of higher operating temperatures and pressures in present aircraft systems. It can generally be used in the same manner as rubber hose. Teflon hose is processed and extruded into tube shape to a desired size. It is covered with stainless steel wire, which is braided over the tube for strength and protection.

Teflon hose is unaffected by any known fuel, petroleum, or synthetic base oils, alcohol, coolants, or solvents commonly used in aircraft. Although it is highly resistant to vibration and fatigue, the principle advantage of this hose is its operating strength.

Identification of Hose

Identification markings consisting of lines, letters, and numbers are printed on the hose (Fig. 6-1). These code markings show such information as hose size, manufacturer, date of manufacture, and pressure and temperature limits. Code markings assist in replacing a hose with one of the same specification or a recommended substitute. Hose suitable for use with phosphate ester base hydraulic fluid will be marked "Skydrol use." In some instances several types of hose might be suitable for the same use. Therefore, in order to make the correct hose selection, always refer to the maintenance or parts manual for the particular aircraft.

Size Designation

The size of flexible hose is determined by its *inside diameter*. Sizes are in $1/16$-inch increments and are identical to corresponding sizes of rigid tubing, with which it can be used.

Identification of Fluid Lines

Fluid lines in aircraft are often identified by markers made up of color codes, words, and geometric symbols. These markers identify each line's function, content, and primary hazard, as well as the direction of fluid flow. Figure 6-2 illustrates the various color codes and symbols used to designate the type of system and its contents.

In addition to the above-mentioned markings, certain lines can be further identified regarding to specific function within a system: DRAIN, VENT, PRESSURE, or RETURN.

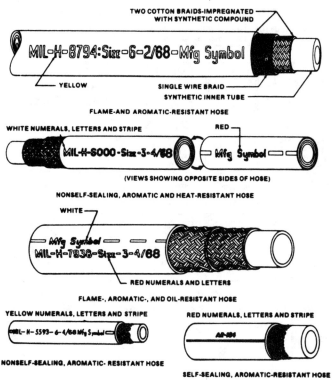

Fig. 6-1. Hose identification markings.

Generally, tapes and decals are placed on both ends of a line and at least once in each compartment through which the line runs. In addition, identification markers are placed immediately adjacent to each valve, regulator, filter, or other accessory within a line. Where paint or tags are used, location requirements are the same as for tapes and decals.

PLUMBING CONNECTIONS

Plumbing connectors, or *fittings*, attach one piece of tubing to another or to system units. There are four types: *flared, flareless, bead and clamp,* and *swaged and welded.* The beaded joint, which requires a bead and a section of hose and hose clamps, is used only in low- or medium-pressure systems, such as vacuum and coolant systems. The flared, flareless, and swaged types can be used as connectors in all systems, regardless of the pressure.

COLORS, FLUID LINES IDENTIFICATION

All bands shall be 1 in. wide and shall encircle the tube.
Bands shall be located near each end of the tube and at such intermediate
points as may be necessary to follow through the system.

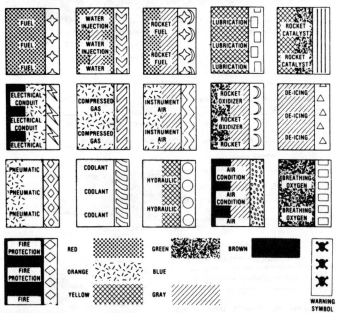

Fig. 6-2. Identification of fluid lines.

Flared-Tube Fittings

A flared-tube fitting consists of a sleeve and a nut, as shown in Fig. 6-3.
The nut fits over the sleeve and, when tightened, draws the sleeve and tubing
flare tightly against a male fitting to form a seal. Tubing used with this type of
fitting must be flared before installation.

The AN standard fitting is the most commonly used flared-tubing assembly
for attaching the tubing to the various fittings required in aircraft plumbing systems. The AN standard fittings include the AN818 nut and AN819 sleeve. The
AN819 sleeve is used with the AN818 coupling nut. All these fittings have
straight threads, but they have different pitch for the various types.

Flared-tube fittings are made of aluminum alloy, steel, or copper base
alloys. For identification purposes, all AN steel fittings are colored black, and all
AN aluminum alloy fittings are colored blue. The AN819 aluminum bronze

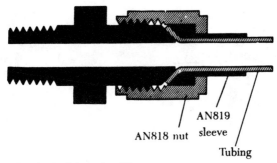

AN819 sleeve

AN818 nut

Tubing

Fig. 6-3. Flared tube fitting using AN parts.

sleeves are cadmium plated and are not colored. The size of these fittings is given in dash numbers, which equal the nominal tube outside diameter (O.D.) in sixteenths of an inch.

Flareless-tube Fittings

The MS (*military standard*) flareless-tube fittings are finding wide application in aircraft plumbing systems. Using this fitting eliminates all tube flaring, yet provides a safe, strong, dependable tube connection (Fig. 6-4).

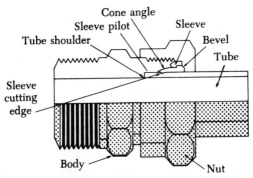

Cone angle

Sleeve pilot

Sleeve

Tube shoulder

Bevel

Tube

Sleeve cutting edge

Body

Nut

Fig. 6-4. A flareless tube fitting.

Tube-Cutting

When cutting tubing, it is important to produce a square end, free of burrs. Tubing can be cut with a tube cutter (Fig. 6-5) or a hacksaw. The cutter can be used with any soft metal tubing, such as copper, aluminum, or aluminum alloy.

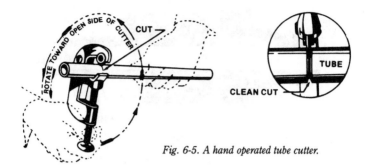

Fig. 6-5. A hand operated tube cutter.

If a tube cutter is not available, or if hard material tubing is to be cut, use a fine-tooth hacksaw, preferably one having 32 teeth per inch. After sawing, file the end of the tube square and smooth, removing all burrs.

Tube Bending

The objective in tube bending is to obtain a smooth bend without flattening the tube. Tubing under three-fourth inch in diameter usually can be bent with a hand bending tool (Fig. 6-6). For larger sizes, $3/4$-inch and over, a factory tube bending machine is usually used.

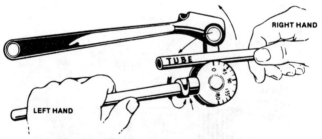

Fig. 6-6. A hand tube bender.

Tube bending machines for all types of tubing are generally used in repair stations and large maintenance shops. With such equipment, proper bends can be made on large diameter tubing and on tubing made from hard material. The production tube bender is one example.

Bend the tubing carefully to avoid excessive flattening, kinking, or wrinkling. A small amount of flattening in bends is acceptable, but the small diameter of the flattened portion must not be less than 75 percent of the original outside diameter. Tubing with flattened, wrinkled or irregular bends should not

be installed. Wrinkled bends usually result from trying to bend thin-wall tubing without using a tube bender. Examples of correct and incorrect tubing bends are shown in Fig. 6-7.

Fig. 6-7. Examples of tube bends.

Tube Flaring

The flaring tool (Fig. 6-8) used for aircraft tubing has male and female dies ground to produce a flare of 35 to 37 degrees. Under no circumstances is it permissible to use an automotive flaring tool that produces a 45-degree flare.

Two kinds of flares are generally used in aircraft plumbing systems: *single* and *double*.

In forming flares, cut the tube ends square, file smooth, remove all burrs and sharp edges, and thoroughly clean. Slip the fitting nut and sleeve on the tube before flaring.

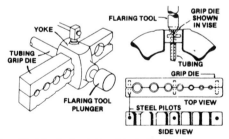

Fig. 6-8. A hand tool for flaring tubing (single flare).

Assembly of Sleeve-Type Fittings

Sleeve-type end fittings for flexible hose are detachable and can be reused if determined to be serviceable. The inside diameter of the fitting is the same as the inside diameter of the hose to which it is attached. Common sleeve-type fittings are shown in Fig. 6-9.

Refer to manufacturers instructions for detailed assembly procedures as outlined in Fig. 6-10.

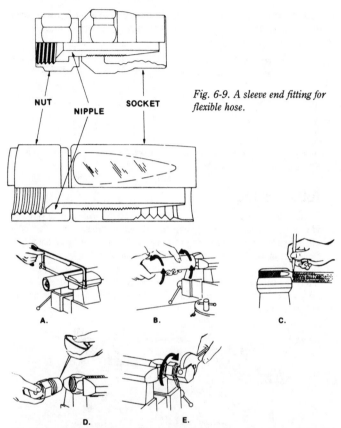

Fig. 6-9. A sleeve end fitting for flexible hose.

Fig. 6-10. Assembly of MS fitting to flexible hose. (Courtesy Aeroquip Corporation.)

Proof-test after Assembly

All flexible hose must be proof-tested after assembly by plugging or capping one end of the hose and applying pressure to the inside of the hose assembly. The proof-test medium can be a liquid or a gas. For example, hydraulic, fuel, and oil lines are generally tested using hydraulic oil or water, whereas air or instrument lines are tested with dry, oil-free air or nitrogen. When testing with a liquid, all trapped air is bled from the assembly prior to tightening the cap or plug. Hose tests, using a gas, are conducted underwater. In all cases, follow

the hose manufacturer's instructions for proof-test pressure and fluid to be used when testing a specific hose assembly.

Place the hose assembly in a horizontal position and observe for leakage while maintaining the test pressure. Proof-test pressures should be maintained for at least 30 seconds.

Installation of Flexible Hose Assemblies

Figure 6-11 shows examples of flexible hose installation.

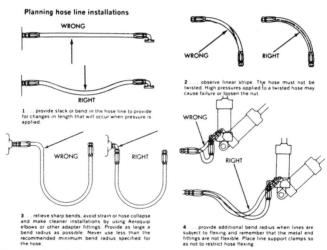

Planning hose line installations

WRONG

RIGHT

1 ... provide slack or bend in the hose line to provide for changes in length that will occur when pressure is applied.

WRONG   RIGHT

2 ... observe linear stripe. The hose must not be twisted. High pressures applied to a twisted hose may cause failure or loosen the nut.

WRONG   RIGHT

WRONG   RIGHT

3 ... relieve sharp bends, avoid strain or hose collapse and make cleaner installations by using Aeroquip elbows or other adapter fittings. Provide as large a bend radius as possible. Never use less than the recommended minimum bend radius specified for the hose.

4 ... provide additional bend radius when lines are subject to flexing and remember that the metal end fittings are not flexible. Place line support clamps so as not to restrict hose flexing.

Fig. 6-11. Installation of flexible hose assemblies. (Courtesy Aeroquip Corporation.)

INSTALLATION OF RIGID TUBING

Never apply compound to the faces of the fitting or the flare because the compound will destroy the metal-to-metal contact between the fitting and flare, a contact that is necessary to create the seal. Be sure that the line assembly is properly aligned before tightening the fittings. Do not pull the installation into place with torque on the nut (Fig. 6-12).

Always tighten fittings to the correct torque value (Fig. 6-13) when installing a tube assembly. Overtightening a fitting might badly damage or completely cut off the tube flare, or it might ruin the sleeve or fitting nut. Failure to tighten sufficiently also can be serious, as this condition might allow the line to blow out of the assembly or to leak under system pressure.

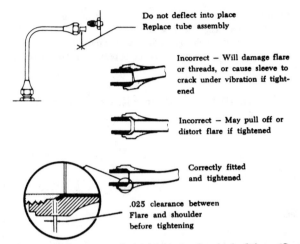

6-12. *Correct and incorrect methods of tightening flared tube fittings. (Courtesy Aeroquip Corporation.)*

The use of torque wrenches and the prescribed torque values prevents overtightening or undertightening. If a tube fitting assembly is tightened properly, it can be removed and retightened many times before reflaring is necessary.

Never select a path that does not require bends in the tubing. A tube cannot be cut or flared accurately enough so that it can be installed without bending and still be free from mechanical strain. Bends are also necessary to permit the tubing to expand or contract under temperature changes and to absorb vibration. If the tube is small (less than 1/4 inch) and can be hand formed, casual bends can be made to allow for this. If the tube must be machine formed, definite bends must be made to avoid a straight assembly.

Start all bends a reasonable distance from the fittings, because the sleeves and nuts must be slipped back during the fabrication of flares and during inspections. In all cases, the new tube assembly should be so formed prior to installation that it will not be necessary to pull or deflect the assembly into alignment by means of the coupling nuts.

Support Clamps

Support clamps are used to secure the various lines to the airframe or power-plant assemblies. Several types of support clamps are used for this purpose, most commonly the *rubber-cushioned* and *plain* clamps. The rubber-cushioned clamp is used to secure lines subject to vibration; the cushioning

TUBING O.D.	FITTING BOLT OR NUT SIZE	ALUMINUM ALLOY TUBING, BOLT, FITTING OR NUT TORQUE INCH-LBS.	STEEL TUBING, BOLT FITTING OR NUT TORQUE INCH-LBS.	HOSE END FITTINGS AND HOSE ASSEMBLIES MS28740 OR EQUIVALENT END FITTING		MINIMUM BEND RADII (INCHES)	
				MINIMUM	MAXIMUM	ALUM. ALLOY 1100 – H14 5052 – O	STEEL
1/8	– 2	20 – 30	90 – 100	70	120	3/8	21/32
3/16	– 3	30 – 40	135 – 150	100	250	7/16	7/8
1/4	– 4	40 – 65	180 – 200	210	420	9/16	11/8
5/16	– 5	60 – 85	270 – 300	300	480	3/4	15/16
3/8	– 6	75 – 125	450 – 500	500	850	15/16	13/4
1/2	– 8	150 – 250	650 – 700	700	1150	11/4	23/16
5/8	– 10	200 – 350	900 – 1000			11/2	25/8
3/4	– 12	300 – 500	1000 – 1100			13/4	
7/8	– 14	500 – 600	1200 – 1400				
1	– 16	500 – 700	1200 – 1400			3	31/2
11/4	– 20	600 – 900	1500 – 1800			33/4	43/8
11/2	– 24	600 – 900				5	51/4
13/4	– 28	850 – 1050				7	61/8
2	– 32	950 – 1150				8	7

Fig. 6-13. Torque values for tightening flared tube fittings.

prevents chafing of the tubing. The plain clamp is used to secure lines in areas not subject to vibration.

A *Teflon-cushioned* clamp is used in areas where the deteriorating effect of Skydrol 500, hydraulic fluid (MIL -0-5606), or fuel is expected. However, because Teflon is less resilient, it does not provide as good a vibration-damping effect as other cushion materials.

Use bonded clamps to secure metal hydraulic, fuel, and oil lines in place. Unbonded clamps should be used only for securing wiring. Remove any paint or anoidizing from the portion of the tube at the bonding clamp location. All plumbing lines must be secured at specified intervals. The maximum distance between supports for rigid tubing is shown in Fig. 6-14.

TUBE OD (IN.)	DISTANCE BETWEEN SUPPORTS (IN.)	
	ALUMINUM ALLOY	STEEL
1/8	9 1/2	11 1/2
3/16	12	14
1/4	13 1/2	16
5/16	15	18
3/8	16 1/2	20
1/2	19	23
5/8	22	25 1/2
3/4	24	27 1/2
1	26 1/2	30

Fig. 6-14. Maximum distance between supports for fluid lines.

7

Control Cables

Three control systems commonly used are cable, push-pull (Fig. 7-1), and torque tube. Many aircraft incorporate control systems that are combinations of all three.

Cables are the most widely used linkage in primary flight control systems. Cable linkage is also used in engine controls, emergency extension systems for the landing gear, and other systems throughout the aircraft.

CABLE ASSEMBLY

The conventional cable assembly consists of flexible cable (Fig. 7-2) *terminals (end fittings)* for attaching to other units, and turnbuckles. Cable tension must be adjusted frequently due to stretching and temperature changes. Aircraft control cables are fabricated from carbon steel or stainless steel.

Fabricating a Cable Assembly

Terminals for aircraft control cables are normally fabricated using three different processes:

- Swaging as used in all modern aircraft.
- Nicropress process.
- Handwoven splice terminal.

Handwoven splices are found on many older aircraft; however, this is a time consuming process, considered unnecessary with the availability of mechanically fabricated splices.

Various swage terminal fittings are shown in Fig. 7-3.

Swaging

Swage terminals, manufactured in accordance with Air Force-Navy Aeronautical Standard Specifications, are suitable for use in civil aircraft up to and

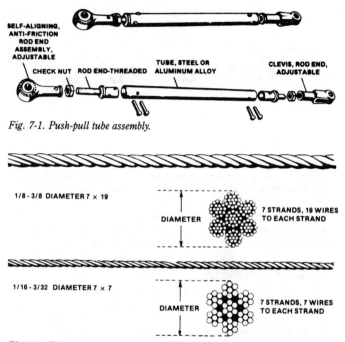

SELF-ALIGNING, ANTI-FRICTION ROD END ASSEMBLY, ADJUSTABLE

CHECK NUT **ROD END-THREADED** **TUBE, STEEL OR ALUMINUM ALLOY** **CLEVIS, ROD END, ADJUSTABLE**

Fig. 7-1. Push-pull tube assembly.

1/8 - 3/8 DIAMETER 7 × 19

DIAMETER

7 STRANDS, 19 WIRES TO EACH STRAND

1/16 - 3/32 DIAMETER 7 × 7

DIAMETER

7 STRANDS, 7 WIRES TO EACH STRAND

Fig. 7-2. The most common aircraft cables are 7 × 7 of medium flexibility and 7 × 19 extra flexibility.

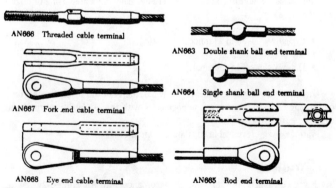

AN666   Threaded cable terminal

AN667   Fork end cable terminal

AN668   Eye end cable terminal

AN663   Double shank ball end terminal

AN664   Single shank ball end terminal

AN665   Rod end terminal

Fig. 7-3. Various types of swage terminal fittings.

including maximum cable loads. When swaging tools are used, it is important that all the manufacturers' instructions, including "go-no-go" dimensions (Fig. 7-4), be followed in detail to avoid defective and inferior swaging. Observance of all instructions should result in a terminal developing the full rated strength of the cable.

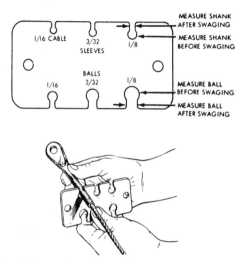

Fig. 7-4. A typical gauge for checking swaged terminals.

Nicropress Process

A patented process using copper sleeves can be used up to the full rated strength of the cable when the cable is looped around a thimble.

Before undertaking a Nicropress splice, the proper tool and sleeve for the cable must be determined based upon the manufacturer's instructions. A typical hand swager is shown in Fig. 7-5.

A typical Nicropress *thimble eye splice* is shown in Fig. 7-6.

To make a satisfactory copper sleeve installation, it is important that the amount of sleeve pressure be kept uniform. The completed sleeves should be checked periodically with the proper gauge. The gauge should be held so that it

Fig. 7-5. A hand operated nicropress swage for cables up to 3/16-inch diameter.

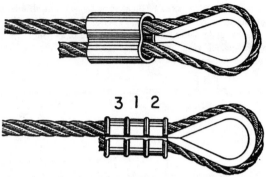

Fig. 7-6. Typical thimble-eye splice. The sleeve should be compressed in the 1-2-3 sequence shown.

contacts the major axis of the sleeve. The compressed portion at the center of the sleeve should enter the gauge opening with very little clearance, as shown in Fig. 7-7. If it does not, the tool must be adjusted accordingly.

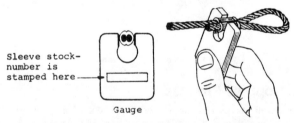

Fig. 7-7. Typical go-no-go gauge for nicopress terminals.

TURNBUCKLES

A turnbuckle assembly is a mechanical screw device consisting of two threaded terminals and a threaded barrel. Figure 7-8 illustrates a typical turnbuckle assembly.

Turnbuckles are fitted in the cable assembly for the purpose of making minor adjustments in cable length and for adjusting cable tension. One of the terminals has right-handed threads and the other has left-handed threads. The barrel has matching right- and left-handed internal threads. The end of the barrel with the left-handed threads can usually be identified by a groove or knurl around that end of the barrel.

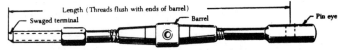

Fig. 7-8. A typical turnbuckle assembly.

Safety Methods for Turnbuckles. After a turnbuckle has been properly adjusted, it must be safetied. There are several methods of safetying turnbuckles; however, only two methods (Figs. 7-9 and 7-10) will be discussed in this chapter. The *clip-locking* method (Fig. 7-9) is used only on modern aircraft. Older aircraft still use turnbuckles that require the *wire-wrapping* method.

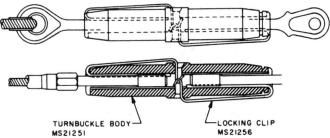

Fig. 7-9. Clip style locking device.

Fig. 7-10. Double wrapping method for safetying turnbuckles.

Double-Wrap Method. Of the methods using safety wire for safetying turnbuckles, the double-wrap method is preferred, although the single-wrap method is satisfactory. The method of double-wrap safetying is shown in Fig. 7-10. Two separate lengths of the proper wire as shown in Fig. 7-11 are used. One end of the wire is run through the hole in the barrel of the turnbuckle. The ends of the wire are bent toward opposite ends of the turnbuckle.

Then the second length of the wire is passed into the hole in the barrel with ends bent along the barrel on the side opposite the first. Then the wires at the end of the turnbuckle are passed in opposite directions through the holes in the turnbuckle eyes or between the jaws of the turnbuckle fork, as applicable.

The laid wires are bent in place before cutting off the wrapped wire. The remaining length of safety wire is wrapped at least four turns around the shank, and cut off. The procedure is repeated at the opposite end of the turnbuckle.

Cable Size (in.)	Type of Wrap	Diameter of Safety Wire	Material (Annealed Condition)
1/16	Single	0.020	Copper, brass.[1]
3/32	Single	0.040	Copper, brass.[1]
1/8	Single	0.040	Stainless steel, Monel and "K" Monel.
1/8	Double	0.040	Copper, brass.[1]
1/8	Single	0.057 min	Copper, brass.[1]
5/32 and greater.	Double	0.040	Stainless steel, Monel and "K" Monel.[1]
5/32 and greater.	Single	0.057 min	Stainless steel, Monel or "K" Monel.[1]
5/32 and greater.	Double	0.051[2]	Copper, brass.

[1] Galvanized or tinned steel, or soft iron wires are also acceptable.
[2] The safty wire holes in 5/32-inch diameter and larger turnbuckle terminals for swaging may be drilled sufficiently to accommodate the double 0.051-inch diameter copper or brass wires when used.

Fig. 7-11. Guide for selecting turnbuckle safety wire.

When a swaged terminal is being safetied, the ends of both wires are passed, if possible, through the hole provided in the terminal for this purpose and both ends are wrapped around the shank as described above.

If the hole is not large enough to allow passage of both wires, the wire should be passed through the hole and looped over the free end of the other wire, and then both ends wrapped around the shank as described.

CABLE TENSION ADJUSTMENT

Control cable tension should be carefully adjusted in accordance with the airframe manufacturer's recommendations. On large aircraft, the temperature of the immediate area should be taken into consideration when using a *tensionmeter* (Fig. 7-12). For long cable sections, the average of two or three temperature readings should be made for extreme surface temperature variations that might be encountered if the aircraft is operated primarily in unusual geographic or climatic conditions such as arctic, arid, or tropic locations. Figure 7-13 shows a typical cable rigging chart.

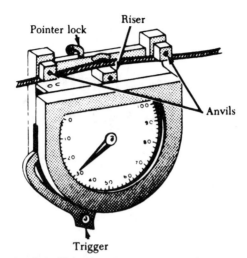

Fig. 7-12. A typical cable tensionmeter.

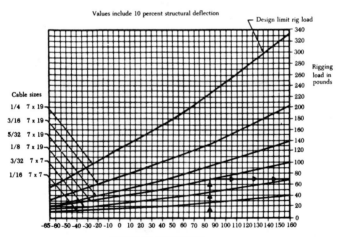

Fig. 7-13. Typical cable rigging chart.

8

Electrical Wiring and Installation

MATERIAL SELECTION

Aircraft service imposes severe environmental conditions on electrical wire. To assure satisfactory service, the wire should be inspected at regular intervals for abrasions, defective insulation, condition of terminal posts, and corrosion under or around swaged terminals.

For the purpose of this discussion, a *wire* is described as a single, solid conductor, or as a stranded conductor covered with an insulating material (Fig. 8-1).

The term *cable*, as used in aircraft electrical installations, includes:

1. Two or more separately insulated conductors in the same jacket (multi-conductor cable).
2. Two or more separately insulated conductors twisted together (twisted pair).
3. One or more insulated conductors, covered with a metallic braided shield (shielded cable).
4. A single insulated center conductor with a metallic braided outer conductor (radio frequency cable). The concentricity of the center conductor and the outer conductor is carefully controlled during manufacture to ensure that they are coaxial.

Wire Size

Wire is manufactured in sizes according to a standard known as the AWG (*American wire gauge*). As shown in Fig. 8-2, the wire diameters become smaller as the gauge numbers become larger. See the appendix for a table of wire gauges.

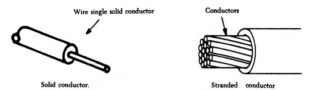

Fig. 8-1. Single solid conductor and a conductor consisting of many strands.

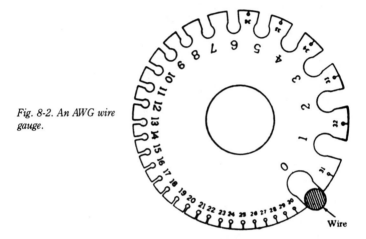

Fig. 8-2. An AWG wire
gauge.

To use the wire gauge, the wire to be measured is inserted in the smallest slot that will just accommodate the bare wire. The gauge number corresponding to that slot indicates the wire size. The slot has parallel sides and should not be confused with the semicircular opening at the end of the slot. The opening simply permits the free movement of the wire all the way through the slot.

Gauge numbers are useful in comparing the diameter of wires, but not all types of wire or cable can be accurately measured with a gauge. Large wires are usually stranded to increase their flexibility. In such cases, the total area can be determined by multiplying the area of one strand (usually computed in circular mils when diameter or gauge number is known) by the number of strands in the wire or cable.

Factors Affecting the Selection of Wire Size

Tables and procedures are available for selecting correct wire sizes. For purposes of this manual, it is assumed that wire sizes were specified by the manufacturer of the aircraft or equipment.

Factors Affecting Selection of Conductor Material

Although silver is the best conductor, high cost limits its use to special circuits where a substance with high conductivity is needed.

The two most generally used conductors are copper and aluminum. Each has characteristics that make its use advantageous under certain circumstances. Also, each has certain disadvantages.

Copper has a higher conductivity; it is more ductile (can be drawn), has relatively high tensile strength, and can be easily soldered. It is more expensive and heavier than aluminum.

Although aluminum has only about 60 percent of the conductivity of copper, it is used extensively. Its lightness makes possible long spans, and its relatively large diameter for a given conductivity reduces *corona*, which is the discharge of electricity from the wire when it has a high potential. The discharge is greater when small diameter wire is used than when large diameter wire is used. Some bus bars are made of aluminum instead of copper where there is a greater radiating surface for the same conductance.

Conductor insulation material varies with the type of installation. Insulation such as rubber, silk, and paper are no longer used extensively in aircraft systems. More common today are such materials as vinyl, cotton, nylon, Teflon, and Rockbestos.

Stripping Insulation

Attachment of wire to connectors or terminals requires the removal of insulation to expose the conductors, commonly known as stripping. When performing the stripping operation, remove no more insulation than is necessary. Stripping can be accomplished in many ways; however, the following basic principles should be practiced:

- Make sure all cutting tools used for stripping are sharp.
- When using special wire stripping tools, adjust the tool to avoid nicking, cutting, or otherwise damaging the strands.
- Automatic stripping tools should be carefully adjusted; the manufacturer's instructions should be followed to avoid nicking, cutting, or otherwise damaging strands. This is especially important for aluminum wires and for copper wires smaller than No. 10. Smaller wires have larger numbers.

A light duty hand-operated wire stripper is shown in Fig. 8-3.

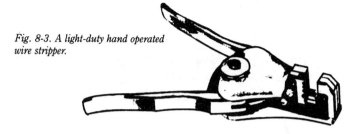

Fig. 8-3. A light-duty hand operated wire stripper.

TERMINALS

Terminals are attached to the ends of electric wires to facilitate connection of the wires to terminal strips or items of equipment. Terminals specifically designed for use with the standard sizes of aircraft wire are available through normal supply channels. Haphazard choice of commercial terminals might contribute to overheated joints, vibration failures, and corrosion difficulties.

For most applications, soldered terminals have been replaced by solderless terminals. The solder process has disadvantages that have been overcome by use of the solderless terminals.

The terminal manufacturer will normally provide a special crimping or swaging tool for joining the solderless terminal to the electric wire. Aluminum wire presents special difficulty in that each individual strand is insulated by an oxide coating. This oxide coating must be broken down in the crimping process and some method employed to prevent its reforming. In all cases, terminal manufacturer's instructions should be followed when installing solderless terminals.

Copper wires are terminated with solderless, preinsulated straight copper terminal *lugs*. The insulation is part of the terminal lug and extends beyond its barrel so that it will cover a portion of the wire insulation, making the use of an insulation sleeve unnecessary (Fig. 8-4).

In addition, preinsulated terminal lugs contain an insulation *rip* (a metal reinforcing sleeve) beneath the insulation for extra gripping strength on the wire insulation. Preinsulated terminals accommodate more than one size of wire; the insulation is usually color-coded to identify the wire sizes that can be terminated with each of the terminal lug sizes.

Some types of uninsulated terminal lugs are insulated after assembly to a wire by means of pieces of transparent flexible tubing called *sleeves*. The sleeve provides electrical and mechanical protection at the connection. When the size of the sleeving used is such that it will fit tightly over the terminal lug, the sleeving need not be tied; otherwise, it should be tied with lacing cord as illustrated in Fig. 8-5.

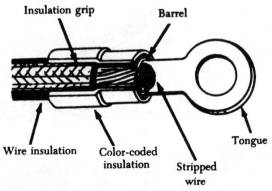

Fig. 8-4. A preinsulated terminal lug.

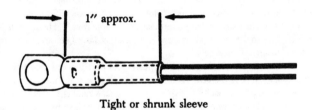

Fig. 8-5. Insulating a terminal lug with a transparent, flexible tubing sleeve.

Aluminum Wire Terminals

The use of aluminum wire in aircraft systems is increasing because of its weight advantage over copper. However, bending aluminum will cause "work hardening" of the metal, making it brittle. This results in failure or breakage of strands much sooner than in a similar case with copper wire. Aluminum also forms a high-resistant oxide film immediately upon exposure to air. To compensate for these disadvantages, it is important to use the most reliable installation procedures.

Only aluminum terminal lugs are used to terminate aluminum wires. All aluminum terminals incorporate an inspection hole (Fig. 8-6), which permits checking the depth of wire insertion. The barrel of aluminum terminal lugs is filled with a petrolatum-zinc dust compound. This compound removes the oxide film from the aluminum by a grinding process during the crimpling operation. The compound will also minimize later oxidation of the completed connection by excluding moisture and air. The compound is retained inside the terminal lug barrel by a plastic or foil seal at the end of the barrel.

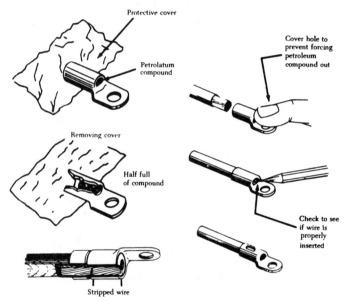

Fig. 8-6. Inserting aluminum wire into aluminum terminal lugs.

Connecting Terminal Lugs to Terminal Blocks

Terminal lugs should be installed on terminal blocks so that they are locked against movement in the direction of loosening (Fig. 8-7).

Terminal blocks are normally supplied with studs secured in place by a plain washer, an external tooth lockwasher, and a nut. In connecting terminals, a recommended practice is to place copper terminal lugs directly on top of the nut, followed with a plain washer and elastic stop nut, or with a plain washer, split steel lockwasher, and plain nut.

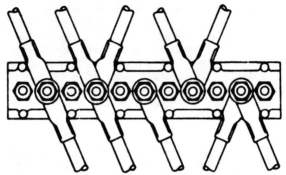

Fig. 8-7. Connecting terminals to a terminal block.

Aluminum terminal lugs should be placed over a plated brass plain washer, followed with another plated brass plain washer, split steel lockwasher, and plain nut or elastic stop nut. The plated brass washer should have a diameter equal to the tongue width of the aluminum terminal lug. The manufacturer's instructions should be consulted for recommended dimensions of these plated brass washers. No washer should be placed in the current path between two aluminum terminal lugs or between two copper terminal lugs. Also, no lockwasher should be placed against the tongue or pad of the aluminum terminal.

To join a copper terminal lug to an aluminum terminal lug, a plated brass plain washer should be placed over the nut that holds the stud in place, followed with the aluminum terminal lug, a plated brass plain washer, the copper terminal lug, plain washer, split steel lockwasher, and plain nut or self-locking, all-metal nut. As a general rule, a torque wrench should be used to tighten nuts to ensure sufficient contact pressure. Manufacturer's instructions provide installation torques for all types of terminals.

Identifying Wire and Cable

Aircraft electrical system wiring and cable can be marked with a combination of letters and numbers to identify the wire, the circuit it belongs to, the gauge number, and other information necessary to relate the wire or cable to a wiring diagram. Such markings are called the *identification code*. There is no standard procedure for marking and identifying wiring; each manufacturer normally develops his own identification code. Wires are usually marked at intervals of not more than 15 inches lengthwise and within 3 inches of each junction or terminating point.

WIRE GROUPS AND BUNDLES

Grouping or bundling certain wires, such as electrically unprotected power wiring and wiring going to duplicate vital equipment, should be avoided.

Wire bundles should generally be less than 75 wires, or 1½ to 2 inches in diameter where practicable. When several wires are grouped at junction boxes, terminal blocks, panels, and the like, the identity of the group within a bundle (Fig. 8-8) can be retained.

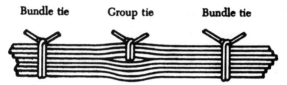

Bundle tie   Group tie   Bundle tie

Fig. 8-8. Groups and bundle ties.

The *flexible nylon cable tie* (Fig. 8-9) has almost completely replaced cord for lacing or tying wire bundles. Nylon cable ties are available in various lengths and are self-locking for a permanent, neat installation.

Single wires or wire bundles should not be installed with excessive slack. Slack between supports should normally not exceed a maximum of ½-inch deflection with normal hand force (Fig. 8-10).

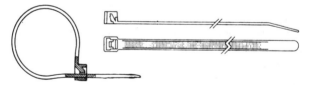

Fig. 8-9. Flexible nylon cable ties have almost completely replaced cord for lacing or tying cable bundles.

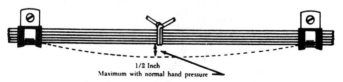

1/2 Inch
Maximum with normal hand pressure

Fig. 8-10. Maximum recommended slack in wire bundles between supports.

Bend Radii

Bends in wire groups or bundles should not be less than 10 times the outside diameter of the wire group or bundle. However, at terminal strips, where wire is suitably supported at each end of the bend, a minimum radius of three times the outside diameter of the wire, or wire bundle, is normally acceptable. There are, of course, exceptions to these guidelines in the case of certain types of cable; for example, coaxial cable should never be bent to a smaller radius than six times the outside diameter.

Routing and Installations

All wiring should be installed so that it is mechanically and electrically sound and neat in appearance. Whenever practicable, wires and bundles should be routed parallel with, or at right angles to, the stringers or ribs of the area involved. An exception to this general rule is coaxial cable, which is routed as directly as possible.

The wiring must be adequately supported throughout its length. A sufficient number of supports must be provided to prevent undue vibration of the unsupported lengths.

When wiring must be routed parallel to combustible fluid or oxygen lines for short distances, as much fixed separation as possible should be maintained. The wires should be on a level with, or above, the plumbing lines. Clamps should be spaced so that if a wire is broken at a clamp it will not contact the line. Where a 6-inch separation is not possible, both the wire bundle and the plumbing line can be clamped to the same structure to prevent any relative motion. If the separation is less than 2 inches, but more than $1/2$ inch, a polyethylene sleeve can be used over the wire bundle to give further protection. Also two cable clamps back-to-back, as shown in Fig. 8-11, can be used to

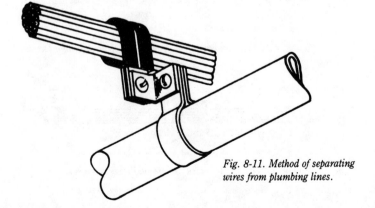

Fig. 8-11. Method of separating wires from plumbing lines.

maintain a rigid separation only, and not for support of the bundle. No wire should be routed so that it is located nearer than $1/2$ inch to a plumbing line. Neither should a wire or wire bundle be supported from a plumbing line that carries flammable fluids or oxygen.

Wiring should be routed to maintain a minimum clearance of at least 3 inches from control cables. If this cannot be accomplished, mechanical guards should be installed to prevent contact between wiring and control cables.

Cable clamps should be installed with regard to the proper angle, as shown in Fig. 8-12. The mounting screw should be above the wire bundle. It is also desirable that the back of the cable clamp rest against a structural member where practicable.

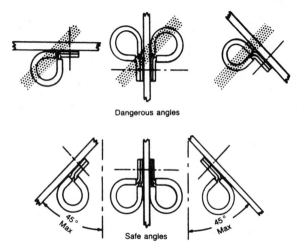

Fig. 8-12. Proper and improper angles for installation of cable clamps.

Care should be taken that wires are not pinched in cable clamps. Where possible, the cables should be mounted directly to structural members, as shown in Figs. 8-13 and 8-14. Clamps can be used with rubber cushions to secure wire bundles to tubular structures. Such clamps must fit tightly, but should not be deformed when locked in place.

Protection Against Chafing

Wires and wire groups should be protected against chafing or abrasion in those locations where contact with sharp surfaces or other wires would damage the insulation. Damage to the insulation can cause short circuits, malfunction, or inadvertent operation of equipment. Cable clamps should be used to

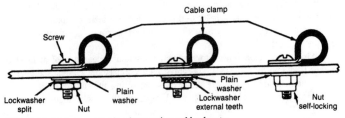

Fig. 8-13. Various methods of mounting cable clamps.

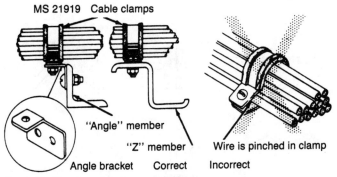

Fig. 8-14. Mounting cable clamp to structure.

support wire bundles at each hole through a bulkhead (Fig. 8-15). If wires come closer than 1/4 inch to the edge of the hole, a suitable grommet is used in the hole as shown in Fig. 8-16.

BONDING AND GROUNDING

Bonding is the electrical connecting of two or more conducting objects not otherwise adequately connected. *Grounding* is the electrical connecting of a conducting object to the primary structure for a return path for current. *Primary structure* is the main frame, fuselage, or wing structure of the aircraft, commonly referred to as *ground*. Bonding and grounding connections are made in aircraft electrical systems to:

- Protect aircraft and personnel against hazards from lightning discharge.
- Provide current return paths.
- Prevent development of radio frequency potentials.
- Protect personnel from shock hazards.
- Provide stability of radio transmission and reception.
- Prevent accumulation of static charge.

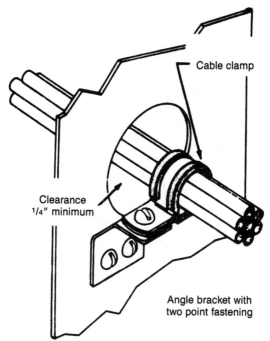

Cable clamp

Clearance
1/4″ minimum

Angle bracket with
two point fastening

Fig. 8-15. Cable clamp at large bulkhead hole.

Bonding jumpers should be made as short as practicable, and installed in such manner that the resistance of each connection does not exceed .003 ohm. The jumper must not interfere with the operation of movable aircraft elements, such as surface controls, nor should normal movement of these elements result in damage to the bonding jumper.

To ensure a low-resistance connection, nonconducting finishes such as paint and anodizing films should be removed from the attachment surface to be contacted by the bonding terminal. Electric wiring should not be grounded directly to magnesium parts.

Electrolytic action might rapidly corrode a bonding connection if suitable precautions are not taken. Aluminum alloy jumpers are recommended for most cases; however, copper jumpers should be used to bond together parts made of stainless steel, cadmium plated steel, copper, brass, or bronze. Where contact between dissimilar metals cannot be avoided, the choice of jumper and hardware should be such that corrosion is minimized, and the part likely to corrode would be the jumper or associated hardware. Figure 8-17 shows the proper

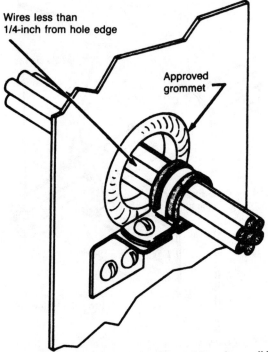

Fig. 8-16. A grommet is used to protect a cable routed through a small bulkhead hole.

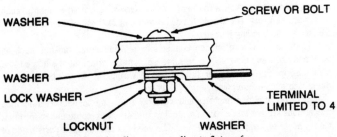

Fig. 8-17. Bolt and nut bonding or grounding to flat surface.

hardware combination for making a bond connection. At locations where finishes are removed, protective finish should be applied to the completed connection to prevent subsequent corrosion.

The use of solder to attach bonding jumpers should be avoided. Tubular members should be bonded by means of clamps to which the jumper is attached. Proper choice of clamp material will minimize the probability of corrosion.

9

Aircraft Drawings

A *drawing* is a method of conveying ideas concerning the construction or assembly of objects. This is done with the help of lines, notes, abbreviations, and symbols. It is very important that the aviation mechanic who is to make or assemble the object understand the meaning of the different lines, notes, abbreviations, and symbols that are used in a drawing.

Although blueprints as such are no longer used, the term *blueprint* or *print* is generally used in place of drawing.

Interpreting a drawing and visualizing the appearance of a part or assembly necessitates an understanding of drafting practices and of the principles of orthographic projection, which establish the methods of illustrating and dimensioning a part.

The following notes are intended to aid the production mechanic only in determining from the print how the part is made, not how the print was drawn.

Although the various manufacturers' drafting systems will differ in detail, there is central agreement in the broad arrangement of drawings. This arrangement serves as an index for the quick location of the specific information required from the print being studied.

A line drawing of the part itself makes up the greater portion of the print; supplemented by dimensions and notes, it completely describes the part. In the lower right-hand corner is a block, referred to as the *legend* or *title block*, containing reference material pertaining to the part. The information given here should be the first portion of the print to be analyzed.

The legend or title block will contain such information as:

Name of the print, which identifies the part.

Number of the print, which indexes this part for filing reference.

Model of the airplane, or of the airplane unit, if an aircraft accessory.

Signatures of draftsmen, engineer, checker, and project engineer.

Material, which notes its form, dimensions, and pertinent specifications.

Finish, which notes any painting, anodizing, plating required, and determines the final condition and appearance of the part. (This information might be indicated by code, which varies with each manufacturer.)

Scale indicated as full, half, etc., giving the proportion of the drawing to the actual part.

Tolerance designates the degree of precision necessary in fabricating the part and guides the inspector in determining the conformance to the print.

Notes that are necessary to label the views or to elaborate any information not sufficiently detailed in the legend are found immediately outside the legend.

Change block is the space allotted to recording design changes. Located directly over the legend or at the top right of the print, it records the date of each change in the drawing and is important when supplying replacement parts for existing aircraft.

The foregoing facts can be applied to interpret the illustrations of the drafting practices that follow.

Orthographic projection is almost universally accepted as the most accurate method to describe fully a part or assembly. Figure 9-1 illustrates the arrangement of views. The front, side, and top views are arranged with the top (or plan) view directly over the front, and the side views directly to the side and in line with the front view.

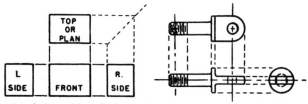

Fig. 9-1. Orthographic projection.

It will be noted, in the part drawn at the right, that only those views needed to describe the part are shown. The left view is omitted because it adds no information not given in the right side view. Generally, three views, or even two or one, might be sufficient. The illustration alone does not, however, fully describe the part if dimensional and material information is lacking. Drawings should be complete and give every requirement for making the part.

The completed drawing (Fig. 9-2) follows such standard drafting room practices as follows:

Index of Lines. Lines are drawn of different boldness and composition to identify the assortment of boundary lines, centerlines, hidden lines, and the like, needed to represent the part (Fig. 9-3).

Dimensioning. It will first be noted that dimensions show size or length of the part, not the size of the drawing. This rule should always be adhered to. Although the drawing, if to full scale, would coincide with the part, it is poor practice to scale a drawing to take a dimension.

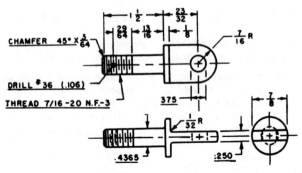

Fig. 9-2. A dimensional drawing.

───────────────────	VISIBLE	LINE
─ ─ ─ ─ ─ ─ ─ ─ ─ ─	INVISIBLE	LINE
───────── ─────	DIMENSION	LINE
───────────────────	EXTENSION	LINE
──── ─ ─ ──── ─ ─ ─	CUTTING	PLANE
──── ─ ─ ──── ─ ─ ─	CENTER	LINE

Fig. 9-3. Index of lines.

The *dimension line* will always be drawn parallel to the dimension indicated and be bounded by extension lines at right angles. The dimension is printed in the break of the dimension line and always reads horizontally regardless of the direction of the dimension line. Dimensions on aircraft drawings are always given in inches, even when the full airplane length is given.

Stations are established at definite points along the fuselage and outward along the wing to aid in locating parts and to make it unnecessary to draw long and overlapping dimension lines. These stations are not placed at random but at such important structural members as ribs and bulkheads. Although in a few drafting systems station designations have no dimensional significance, fuselage stations usually are measurements in inches from the nose of the aircraft aft (from the fire wall, if a single-engine aircraft); wing stations are from the centerline of the airplane measuring outboard (Fig. 9-4).

Station lines will be found on other drawings than that of the completed airplane; for example, the drawing of an aileron will show station lines at rib locations. The station line dimensions will, however, be dimensioned from the

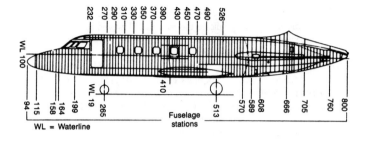

WL = Waterline

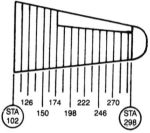

Fig. 9-4. Examples of station designation.

centerline of the airplane, as on the wing, and will coincide with the same stations along the wing.

Sectional views (Fig. 9-5) are drawn to show the cross-sectional profile of a part. The location from which this view is taken is indicated by a cutting plane line that suggests that the part is cut in two at this line. The view of the exposed surface is rotated to an end view. The arrows at the ends of the cutting plane point toward the surface to be shown.

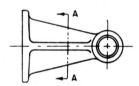

Fig. 9-5. A sectional view.

SECTION A-A

The sectional view is crosshatched according to the drafting room practices of the manufacturer to indicate the material. However, to eliminate confusing lines, sheet metal and such thin sections are not crosshatched.

The illustration of view B-B (Fig. 9-6) is another application of the cutting plane line. Not actually a cross section of a part, it is used to eliminate the necessity of drawing a rotated view of the complete part. Here only the approximate portion represented by the length of the cutting plane is given in a rotated view to show the detail of the splice in this particular part. The letters used in the illustration do not identify the type of view but alphabetically identify and locate the sectional view on the principal view.

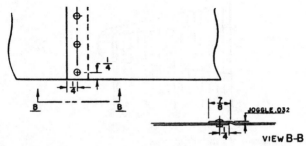

Fig. 9-6. Example of sectional view of thin sheet structure.

WORKING DRAWINGS

Working drawings must give such information as size of the object and all of its parts, its shape and that of all of its parts, specifications as to the material to be used, how the material is to be finished, how the parts are to be assembled, and any other information essential to making and assembling the particular object.

Working drawings can be divided into three classes: *detail*, *assembly*, and *installation*.

Detail Drawing. A detail drawing is a description of a single part, given in such a manner as to describe by lines, notes, and symbols the specifications as to size, shape, material, and methods of manufacture that are to be used in making the part. Detail drawings are usually rather simple and, when single parts are small, several detail drawings might be shown on the same sheet or print.

Assembly Drawing. An assembly drawing is a description of an object made up of two or more parts. It describes the object by giving, in a general way, the size and shape. Its primary purpose is to show the relationship of the various parts. An assembly drawing is usually more complex than a detail drawing, and is often accompanied by detail drawings of various parts.

Installation Drawing. An installation drawing is one that includes all necessary information for a part or an assembly of parts in the final position in the aircraft. It shows the dimensions necessary for the location of specific parts with relation to the other parts and reference dimensions that are helpful in later work in the shop.

PICTORIAL DRAWINGS

A pictorial drawing is similar to a photograph. It shows an object as it appears to the eye, but it is not satisfactory for showing complex forms and shapes. Pictorial drawings are useful in showing the general appearance of an object and are used extensively with orthographic projection drawings. Pictorial drawings are used in maintenance and overhaul manuals.

REFERENCE LINES

There are various numbering systems in use to facilitate location of specific wing ribs, fuselage bulkheads, or other structural members on an aircraft. Most manufacturers use some system of station marking; for example, the

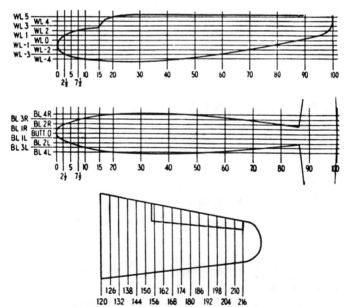

Fig. 9-7. Fuselage stations, waterlines, and butt lines and wing stations.

nose of the aircraft might be designated zero station, and all other stations are measured distances in inches behind the zero station. Thus, when a drawing (blueprint) reads "fuselage frame station 90," that particular frame station can be located 90 inches behind the nose of the aircraft. Figure 9-7 shows a typical station diagram.

To locate structures to the left or right of the centerline of the aircraft, many manufacturers consider the centerline as a zero station for structural member location to its left or right. With such a system the stabilizer ribs can be designated as being a certain number of inches left or right of the aircraft centerline.

The applicable manufacturer's numbering system and abbreviated designations or symbols should always be reviewed before attempting to locate a structural member.

The following list includes location designations typical of those used by many manufacturers.

Fuselage Stations (F.S.)

Fuselage stations are numbered in inches from a reference or zero point known as the *reference datum*. The reference datum is an imaginary vertical plane at or near the nose of the aircraft from which all horizontal distances are measured.

Buttock or Butt Lines (B.L.)

Butt lines are width measurements left or right of the vertical centerline.

Water Lines (W.L.)

Water lines are height measurements perpendicular from a horizontal plane located at a fixed location (within the fuselage as in Fig. 9-7, or a fixed distance below the bottom of the fuselage).

Wing Station (W.S.), Horizontal Stabilizer Stations (H.S.S.)

These stations are measured left or right of the aircraft centerline or sometimes referenced to the root of the wing or horizontal stabilizer.

RIVET SYMBOLS USED ON DRAWINGS (BLUEPRINTS)

Rivet locations are shown on drawings by symbols. These symbols provide the necessary information by the use of code numbers or code letters or a com-

bination of both. The meaning of the code numbers and code letters is explained in the general notes section of the drawing on which they appear.

The rivet code system has been standardized by the National Aerospace Standards Committee (NAS Standard) and has been adopted by most major companies in the aircraft industry. This system has been assigned the number NAS523 in the NAS Standard book.

The NAS523 basic rivet symbol consists of two lines crossing at 90 degrees, which form four quadrants. Code letters and code numbers are placed in these quadrants to give the desired information about the rivet. Each quadrant has been assigned a name: northwest (NW), northeast (NE), southwest (SW), and southeast (SE) (Fig. 9-8).

Fig. 9-8. Basic rivet symbol quadrant configuration.

The rivet type, head type, size, material, and location are shown on the field of the drawing by means of the rivet code, with one exception. Rivets to be installed flush on both sides are not coded, but are called out and detailed on the drawing. An explanation of the rivet codes for each type of rivet used is shown on the field of the drawing. Figure 9-9 shows examples of rivet coding on the drawing and Fig. 9-10 is a sample of rivet coding.

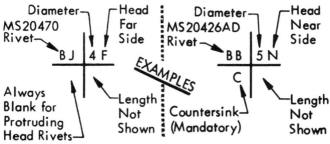

Fig. 9-9. Examples of rivet coding on a drawing.

Hole and countersink dimensions for solid shank and blind rivets are omitted on all drawings because it is understood that the countersink angle is 100 degrees, and the countersink should be of such depth that the fastener fits flush with the surface after driving.

CODE	BASIC PART NO.	MATERIAL	DESCRIPTION OF RIVET
BA	MS20426A	1100F	Solid, 100° Flush
BB	MS20426AD	2117-T3	Solid, 100° Flush
CY	MS20426DD	2024-T31	Solid, 100° Flush
BH	MS20470A	1100F	Solid, Universal Head
BJ	MS20470AD	2117-T3	Solid, Universal Head
CX	MS20470DD	2024-T31	Solid, Universal Head
AAR	NAS1738E	5056	Blind, Protruding Head
AAP	NAS1738M	MONEL	Blind, Protruding Head
AAV	NAS1739E	5056	Blind, 100° Flush
AAW	NAS1739M	MONEL	Blind, 100° Flush

Fig. 9-10. Typical examples of rivet coding. This list will vary according to requirements of each manufacturer.

When there are a number of rivets in a row that are identical, the rivet code is shown for the first and last rivet in the row only, and an arrow will show the direction in which the rivet row runs. The location of the rivets between the rivet codes are marked only with crossing centerlines, as shown in Fig. 9-11.

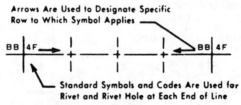

Fig. 9-11. Method of illustrating rivet code and location where there are a number of identical rivets in a row.

10

Standard Parts

STANDARD PARTS IDENTIFICATION

Because the manufacture of aircraft requires a large number of miscellaneous small fasteners and other items usually called *hardware*, some degree of standardization is required. These standards have been derived by the various military organizations and described in detail in a set of specifications with applicable identification codes. These military standards have been universally adopted by the civil aircraft industry.

The derivation of a uniform standard is by necessity an evolutionary process. Originally, each of the military services derived its own standards. The old Army Air Corps set up AC (Air Corps) standards whereas the Navy used NAF (Naval Aircraft Factory) standards. In time, these were consolidated into AN (Air Force-Navy) standards and NAS (National Aerospace Standards). Still later these were consolidated into MS (Military Standard) designations.

At present, the three most common standards are:

- AN, Air Force-Navy.
- MS, Military Standard.
- NAS, National Aerospace Standards.

The aircraft mechanic will also occasionally be confronted with the following standard parts on older aircraft:

- AC (Air Corps).
- NAF (Naval Aircraft Factory).

Each of these standard parts is identified by its specification number and various dash numbers and letters to fully describe its name, size and material.

Additional information on AN, MS, NAS, as well as AMS and AND specifications, and a schedule of prices for specification sheets can be obtained from:

National Standards Association
1321 Fourteenth St. N.W.
Washington, D.C. 20005

Most airframe manufacturers have need for special small parts and use their own series of numbers and specifications. However, they use the universal standard parts wherever practicable.

Because the purpose of this *Standard Aircraft Handbook* is to provide the mechanic with a handy reference, only the most common standard parts are mentioned here with sufficient information to identify them.

More complete information on standard hardware is available from catalogs provided by the many aircraft parts suppliers.

STANDARD PARTS ILLUSTRATIONS

AN standard parts along with their equivalent and/or superceding MS numbers are shown in the following pages.

AN 255 SCREW—NECKED

AN 256 NUT—SELF LOCK (Rt. Angle Plate)

AN 257 HINGE—CONTINUOUS

AN 276 JOINT—BALL & SOCKET

AN 280 KEY—WOODRUFF

AN 295 CUP—OIL

AN 310 NUT—CASTLE (Air Frame)

AN 315 NUT—PLAIN (Air Frame)

AN 316 NUT—CHECK

AN 320 NUT—CASTLE, SHEAR

AN 335 NUT—PL. HEX (NC) (Semi-Fin)

AN 340 NUT—HEX, MACH. SCREW (NC)

AN 341 NUT—HEX, BRASS (Elec.)

AN 345 NUT—HEX, MACH. SCREW (NF)

AN 350 NUT—WING

AN 355 NUT—SLOTTED (Engine)

USAF 356 NUT—PAL

AN Guide

AN 3 thru AN 20 BOLT—HEX HD. AIRCRAFT

AN 21 thru AN 36 BOLT—CLEVIS

AN 42 thru AN 49 BOLT—EYE

AN 73 thru AN 81 BOLT—DR HD (Engine)

AN 100 THIMBLE—CABLE

AN 115 SHACKLE—CABLE

AN 116 SHACKLE—SCREW PIN

AN 155 BARREL—TURNBUCKLE

AN 161 FORK—TURNBUCKLE

AN 162 FORK—TURNBUCKLE (For Bearing)

AN 165 EYE—TURNBUCKLE (For Pin)

AN 170 EYE—TURNBUCKLE (For Cable)

AN 173 thru AN 186 BOLT, CLOSE TOL.

AN 210 thru AN 221 PULLEY—CONTROL

AN 253 PIN—HINGE

AN 254 SCREW—THUMB, NECKED

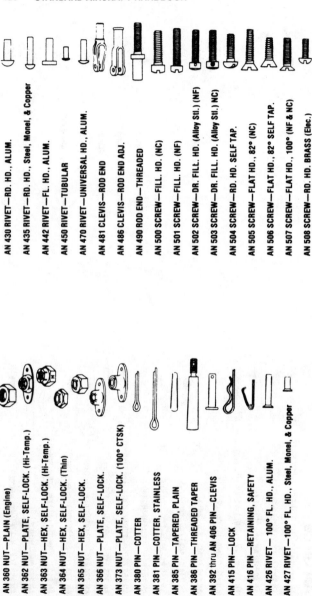

AN 430 RIVET—RD. HD., ALUM.

AN 435 RIVET—RD. HD., Steel, Monel, & Copper

AN 442 RIVET—FL. HD., ALUM.

AN 450 RIVET—TUBULAR

AN 470 RIVET—UNIVERSAL HD., ALUM.

AN 481 CLEVIS—ROD END

AN 486 CLEVIS—ROD END ADJ.

AN 490 ROD END—THREADED

AN 500 SCREW—FILL. HD. (NC)

AN 501 SCREW—FILL. HD. (NF)

AN 502 SCREW—DR. FILL. HD. (Alloy Stl.) (NF)

AN 503 SCREW—DR. FILL. HD. (Alloy Stl.) NC)

AN 504 SCREW—RD. HD. SELF TAP.

AN 505 SCREW—FLAT HD., 82° (NC)

AN 506 SCREW—FLAT HD., 82° SELF TAP.

AN 507 SCREW—FLAT HD., 100° (NF & NC)

AN 508 SCREW—RD. HD. BRASS (Elec.)

AN 360 NUT—PLAIN (Engine)

AN 362 NUT—PLATE, SELF-LOCK. (Hi-Temp.)

AN 363 NUT—HEX, SELF-LOCK. (Hi-Temp.)

AN 364 NUT—HEX, SELF-LOCK. (Thin)

AN 365 NUT—HEX, SELF-LOCK.

AN 366 NUT—PLATE, SELF-LOCK.

AN 373 NUT—PLATE, SELF-LOCK. (100° CTSK)

AN 380 PIN—COTTER

AN 381 PIN—COTTER, STAINLESS

AN 385 PIN—TAPERED, PLAIN

AN 386 PIN—THREADED TAPER

AN 392 thru AN 406 PIN—CLEVIS

AN 415 PIN—LOCK

AN 416 PIN—RETAINING, SAFETY

AN 426 RIVET—100° FL. HD., ALUM.

AN 427 RIVET—100° FL. HD., Steel, Monel, & Copper

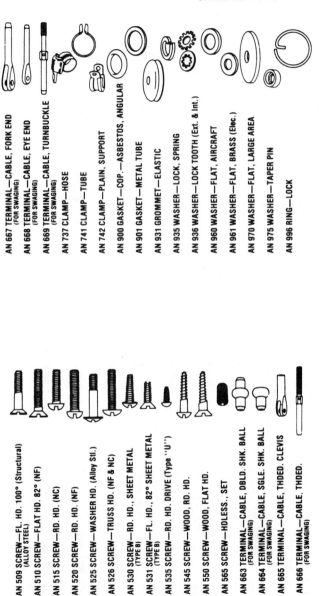

AN 667 TERMINAL—CABLE, FORK END (FOR SWAGING)

AN 668 TERMINAL—CABLE, EYE END (FOR SWAGING)

AN 669 TERMINAL—CABLE, TURNBUCKLE (FOR SWAGING)

AN 737 CLAMP—HOSE

AN 741 CLAMP—TUBE

AN 742 CLAMP—PLAIN, SUPPORT

AN 900 GASKET—COP.—ASBESTOS, ANGULAR

AN 901 GASKET—METAL TUBE

AN 931 GROMMET—ELASTIC

AN 935 WASHER—LOCK, SPRING

AN 936 WASHER—LOCK TOOTH (Ext. & Int.)

AN 960 WASHER—FLAT, AIRCRAFT

AN 961 WASHER—FLAT, BRASS (Elec.)

AN 970 WASHER—FLAT, LARGE AREA

AN 975 WASHER—TAPER PIN

AN 996 RING—LOCK

AN 509 SCREW—FL. HD. 100° (Structural) (ALLOY STEEL)

AN 510 SCREW—FLAT HD. 82° (NF)

AN 515 SCREW—RD. HD. (NC)

AN 520 SCREW—RD. HD. (NF)

AN 525 SCREW—WASHER HD. (Alloy Stl.)

AN 526 SCREW—TRUSS HD. (NF & NC)

AN 530 SCREW—RD. HD., SHEET METAL (TYPE B)

AN 531 SCREW—FL. HD., 82° SHEET METAL (TYPE B)

AN 535 SCREW—RD. HD. DRIVE (Type "U")

AN 545 SCREW—WOOD, RD. HD.

AN 550 SCREW—WOOD, FLAT HD.

AN 565 SCREW—HDLESS., SET

AN 663 TERMINAL—CABLE, DBLD. SHK. BALL (FOR SWAGING)

AN 664 TERMINAL—CABLE, SGLE. SHK. BALL (FOR SWAGING)

AN 665 TERMINAL—CABLE, THDED. CLEVIS

AN 666 TERMINAL—CABLE, THDED. (FOR SWAGING)

M S

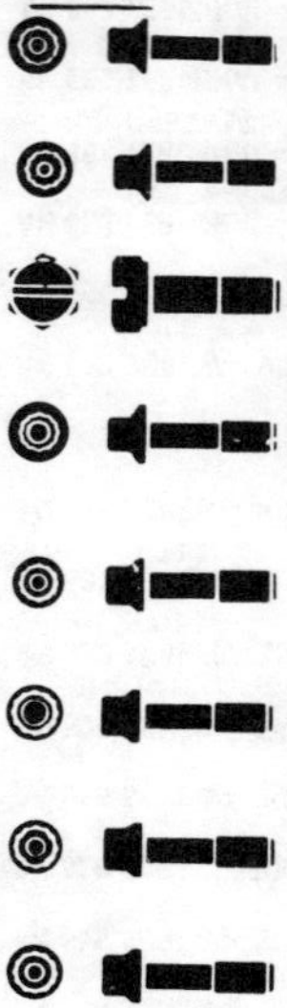

MS 9033 thru MS 9039
MS 9060 thru MS 9066
12 Point Bolt - A286 - 1200°
130,000 psi Min. T.S.

MS 9088 thru MS 9094
12 Point Bolt - Steel
125,000 psi Min T S

MS 9122 thru MS 9123
Slotted Hex Head Mach Screw
125,000 psi Min. T S

MS 9146 thru MS 9152
MS 9157 thru MS 9163
MS 9169 thru MS 9175
12 Point Bolt
125,000 psi Min T S

MS 9177 thru MS 9178
12 Point Bolt, A286 - 1200
130,000 psi Min T S

MS 9183 thru MS 9186
MS 9189 thrus MS 9192
12 Point Bolt - Steel
125,000 psi Min T S

MS 9187 thru MS 9188
12 Point Bolt - A286 - 1200°
130,000 psi Min T S.

MS 9224
12 Point Bolt - A286 - 1200°
130,000 psi Min T S

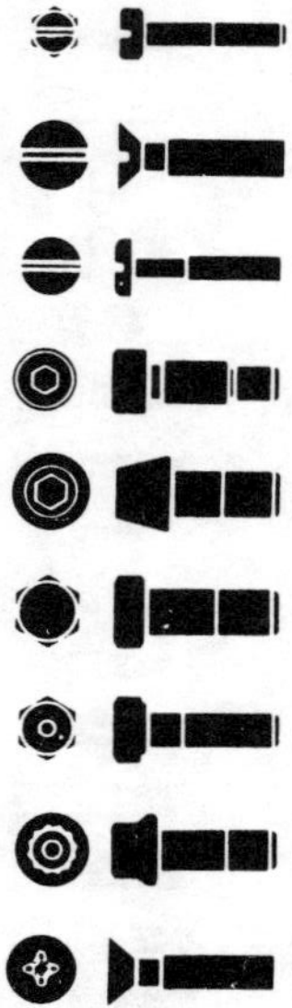

MS 9316 thru MS 9317
Slotted Hex Head Mach Screw
140,000 psi Min T S

MS 16219
Flat Countersunk Head, Slotted,
Nonmagnetic, CRES Mach Screw

MS 16200
Pan Head Slotted CRES
Mach Screw

MS 16637 thru MS 16638
Screw Shoulder, Socket Head, Hex
Alloy Steel, uncoated, Cad or Zinc

MS 20004 thru MS 20024
Internal Wrenching Bolt
160,000 psi Min T S.

MS 20033 thru MS 20046
Hex Head Bolt - 1200
110,000 psi Min T S

MS 20073 thru MS 20074
Hex Head Bolt
125,000 psi Min. T S

MS 21250
12 Point Bolt
180,000 psi Min. T.S.

MS 24583
Screw, Mach. Flat Countersunk Cros
Recessed, Carbon Steel, Cadmium

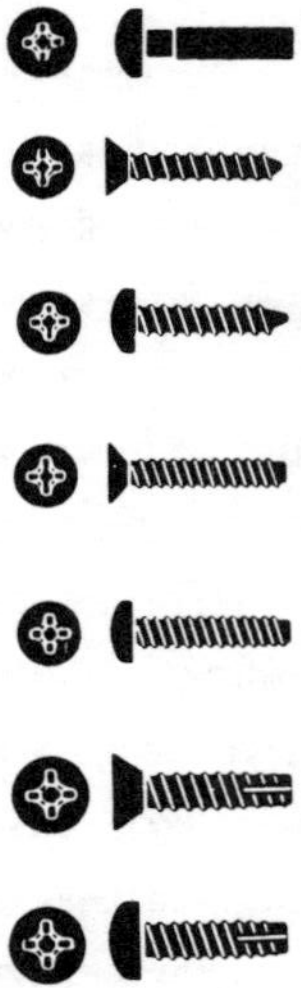

MS 24584
Screw Mach. Pan Head
Cross Recessed, Carbon Steel, Cad

MS 24615 thru MS 24616
Screw, Tapping, Thread Forming, Type A,
Flat Countersunk, Cross Recessed, Carbor
Steel, Cad Plated or CRES

MS 24617 thru MS 24618
Screw, Tapping, Thread Forming, Type A,
Pan Head, Cross Recessed, Carbon Steel,
Cad Plated or CRES

MS 24619 thru MS 24620
Screw, Tapping, Thread Forming, Type B,
Flat Countersunk, Cross Recessed, Carbor
Steel, Cad. Plated or CRES

MS 24621 thru MS 24622
Pan Head, Self Tapping, Thread Forming,
Cross Recess, Type B, Carbon Steel,
Cad. Plated or CRES

MS 24623 thru MS 24624
Flat Head, Self Tapping, Thread Cutting,
Cross Recess, Type BF, BG or BT;
Carbon Steel, Cad. Plated or CRES

MS 24625 thru MS 24626
Pan Head, Self Tapping, Thread Cutting,
Cross Recess, Type BF, BG or BT;
Carbon Steel, Cad. Plated or CRES

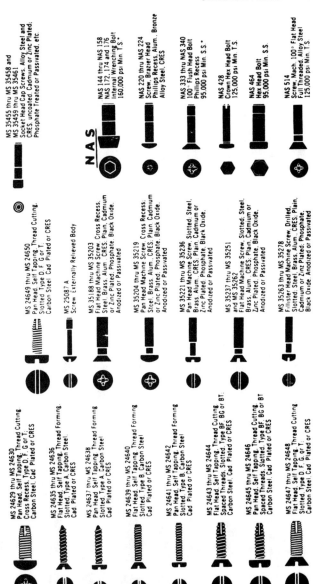

MS 24629 thru MS 24630
Pan Head, Self Tapping, Thread Cutting.
Cross Recess, Type D, F, G or T.
Carbon Steel. Cad Plated or CRES

MS 24635 thru MS 24636
Flat Head, Self Tapping, Thread Forming.
Slotted, Type A. Carbon Steel.
Cad Plated or CRES

MS 24637 thru MS 24638
Pan Head, Self Tapping, Thread Forming
Slotted Type A. Carbon Steel
Cad Plated or CRES

MS 24639 thru MS 24640
Flat Head, Self Tapping, Thread Forming
Slotted Type B. Carbon Steel
Cad Plated or CRES

MS 24641 thru MS 24642
Pan Head, Self Tapping, Thread Forming
Slotted Type B. Carbon Steel
Cad Plated or CRES

MS 24643 thru MS 24644
Flat Head, Self Tapping, Thread Cutting.
Spaced Threads Slotted. Type BF, BG or BT.
Carbon Steel. Cad Plated or CRES

MS 24645 thru MS 24646
Pan Head, Self Tapping, Thread Cutting.
Spaced Threads, Slotted. Type BF, BG or BT
Carbon Steel. Cad Plated or CRES

MS 24647 thru MS 24648
Flat Head, Self Tapping, Thread Cutting
Slotted, Type D, F, G or T.
Carbon Steel. Cad Plated or CRES

MS 24649 thru MS 24650
Pan Head, Self Tapping, Thread Cutting.
Slotted Type D, F, G or T.
Carbon Steel. Cad Plated or CRES

MS 25087 A
Screw, Externally Relieved Body

MS 35188 thru MS 35203
Flat Head Machine Screw. Cross Recess.
Steel, Brass Alum. CRES. Plain, Cadmium
or Zinc Plated. Phosphate. Black Oxide.
Anodized or Passivated

MS 35204 thru MS 35219
Pan Head Machine Screw. Cross Recess.
Steel, Brass Alum. CRES. Plain, Cadmium
or Zinc Plated. Phosphate. Black Oxide.
Anodized or Passivated

MS 35221 thru MS 35236
Pan Head Machine Screw. Slotted. Steel,
Brass, Alum. CRES. Plain, Cadmium or
Zinc Plated. Phosphate. Black Oxide.
Anodized or Passivated

MS 35237 thru MS 35251
and MS 35262
Flat Head Machine Screw. Slotted. Steel,
Brass, Alum. CRES. Plain, Cadmium or
Zinc Plated. Phosphate. Black Oxide.
Anodized or Passivated

MS 35263 thru MS 35278
Fillister Head Machine Screw. Drilled.
Slotted. Steel, Brass, Alum. CRES. Plain,
Cadmium or Zinc Plated. Phosphate.
Black Oxide. Anodized or Passivated

MS 35455 thru MS 35458 and
MS 35459 thru MS 35461
Socket Head Cap Screws. Alloy Steel and
CRES. uncoated. Cadmium or Zinc Plated.
Phosphate Treated or Passivated. etc.

NAS

NAS 144 thru NAS 158
NAS 172, 174 and 176
Internal Wrenching Bolt
160,000 psi Min T.S.

NAS 220 thru NAS 224
Screw, Brazier Head
Phillips Recess. Alum. Bronze
Alloy Steel. CRES

NAS 333 thru NAS 340
100 Flush Head Bolt
Phillips Recess
95,000 psi Min S.S.

NAS 428
Crown Hex Head Bolt
125,000 psi Min T.S.

NAS 464
Hex Head Bolt
95,000 psi Min S.S.

NAS 514
Screw, Mach. 100° Flat Head
Full Threaded. Alloy Steel
125,000 psi Min T.S.

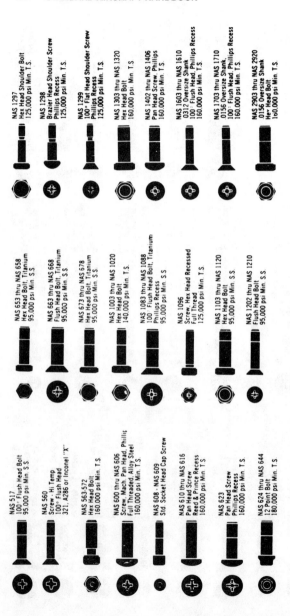

NAS 1297
Hex Head Shoulder Bolt
125,000 psi Min. T.S.

NAS 1298
Brazier Head Shoulder Screw
Phillips Recess
125,000 psi Min. T.S.

NAS 1299
100° Flat Head Shoulder Screw
Phillips Recess
125,000 psi Min. T.S.

NAS 1303 thru NAS 1320
Hex Head Bolt
160,000 psi Min. T.S.

NAS 1402 thru NAS 1406
Pan Head Screw, Phillips
160,000 psi Min. T.S.

NAS 1603 thru NAS 1610
.0312 Oversize Shank
100° Flush Head, Phillips Recess
160,000 psi Min. T.S.

NAS 1703 thru NAS 1710
.0156 Oversize Shank
100° Flush Head, Phillips Recess
160,000 psi Min. T.S.

NAS 2903 thru NAS 2920
.0156 Oversize Shank
Hex Head Bolt
160,000 psi Min. T.S.

NAS 653 thru NAS 658
Hex Head Bolt, Titanium
95,000 psi Min. S.S.

NAS 663 thru NAS 668
Flush Head Bolt, Titanium
95,000 psi Min. S.S.

NAS 673 thru NAS 678
Hex Head Bolt, Titanium
95,000 psi Min. S.S.

NAS 1003 thru NAS 1020
Hex Head Bolt
140,000 psi Min. T.S.

NAS 1083 thru NAS 1088
100° Flush Head Bolt, Titanium
Phillips Recess
95,000 psi Min. T.S.

NAS 1096
Screw, Hex Head Recessed
Full Thread
125,000 psi Min. T.S.

NAS 1103 thru NAS 1120
Hex Head Bolt
95,000 psi Min. S.S.

NAS 1202 thru NAS 1210
Flush Head Bolt
95,000 psi Min. S.S.

NAS 517
100° Flush Head Bolt
95,000 psi Min. S.S.

NAS 560
Screw - Hi Temp
100° Flush Head
321, A286 or Inconel "X"

NAS 563-572
Hex Head Bolt
160,000 psi Min. T.S.

NAS 600 thru NAS 606
Screw, Mach Pan Head, Phillip
Full Threaded, Alloy Steel
160,000 psi Min. T.S.

NAS 608 - NAS 609
Std Socket Head Cap Screw

NAS 610 thru NAS 616
Pan Head Screw
Reed & Prince Recess
160,000 psi Min. T.S.

NAS 623
Pan Head Screw
Phillips Recess
160,000 psi Min. T.S.

NAS 624 thru NAS 644
12 Point Bolt
180,000 psi Min. T.S.

AN3 – AN20 GENERAL-PURPOSE BOLT

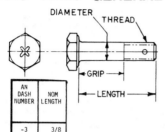

DIAMETER · THREAD · GRIP · LENGTH

AN DASH NUMBER	NOM LENGTH
-3	3/8
-4	1/2
-5	5/8
-6	3/4
-7	7/8
-10	1-
-11	1-1/8
-12	1-1/4
-13	1-3/8
-14	1-1/2
-15	1-5/8
-16	1-3/4
-17	1-7/8
-20	2-
-21	2-1/8
-22	2-1/4
-23	2-3/8
-24	2-1/2
-25	2-5/8
-26	2-3/4
-27	2-7/8
-30	3-
-31	3-1/8
-32	3-1/4
-33	3-3/8
-34	3-1/2
-35	3-5/8
-36	3-3/4
-37	3-7/8
-40	4-

NON-CORROSIVE-RESISTANT STEEL MACHINE BOLTS SHOWN, MEET SPECIFICATION MIL-B-6812. CADMIUM PLATED TO SPECIFICATION QQ-P-416. DRILLED HEAD BOLTS ARE COUNTERSINK DRILLED.

PART NUMBER EXAMPLES FOR A CADMIUM PLATED STEEL BOLT HAVING A DIAMETER OF 3/8" A NOMINAL LENGTH OF 1":
AN6-10   (DRILLED SHANK)
AN6H10   (DRILLED HEAD AND SHANK)
AN6-10A (UNDRILLED)
AN6H10A (DRILLED HEAD)

The general-purpose structural bolt (AN3 through AN20) is identified by a cross or asterisk. Nominal lengths are shown above and grip and length and tolerances are shown below. Examples shown are through AN8 (1/2") and lengths through -40 (4"). Larger diameters are identified by sixteenths of an inch (AN16, 16/16 or 1" diameter). Lengths are correspondingly coded in 8ths of an inch (AN63 = 6" + 3/8" or 6 3/8").

DASH NO.	AN3 GRIP ±1/64	AN3 LENGTH +1/32 -1/64	AN4 GRIP ±1/64	AN4 LENGTH +1/32 -1/64	AN5 GRIP ±1/64	AN5 LENGTH +1/32 -1/64	AN6 GRIP ±1/64	AN6 LENGTH +1/32 -1/64	AN7 GRIP ±1/64	AN7 LENGTH +1/32 -1/64	AN8 GRIP ±1/64	AN8 LENGTH +1/32 -1/64
3	1/16	15/32	1/16	15/32								
4	1/8	17/32	1/16	17/32								
5	1/4	21/32	3/16	21/32	1/16	19/32						
6	3/8	25/32	5/16	25/32	5/16	27/32	1/16	45/64	1/16	23/32		
7	1/2	29/32	7/16	29/32	7/16	31/32	5/16	61/64	5/16	31/32	3/16	31/32
10	5/8	1-1/32	9/16	1-1/32	9/16	1-3/32	7/16	1-5/64	7/16	1-3/32	5/16	1-3/32
11	3/4	1-5/32	11/16	1-5/32	11/16	1-7/32	9/16	1-13/64	9/16	1-7/32	7/16	1-7/32
12	7/8	1-9/32	13/16	1-9/32	13/16	1-11/32	11/16	1-21/64	11/16	1-11/32	9/16	1-11/32
13	1	1-13/32	15/16	1-13/32	15/16	1-15/32	13/16	1-29/64	13/16	1-15/32	11/16	1-15/32
14	1-1/8	1-17/32	1-1/16	1-17/32	1-1/16	1-19/32	15/16	1-37/64	15/16	1-19/32	13/16	1-19/32
15	1-1/4	1-21/32	1-3/16	1-21/32	1-3/16	1-23/32	1-1/16	1-45/64	1-1/16	1-23/32	15/16	1-23/32
16	1-3/8	1-25/32	1-5/16	1-25/32	1-5/16	1-27/32	1-3/16	1-53/64	1-3/16	1-27/32	1-1/16	1-27/32
17	1-1/2	1-29/32	1-7/16	1-29/32	1-7/16	1-31/32	1-5/16	1-61/64	1-5/16	1-31/32	1-3/16	1-31/32
20	1-5/8	2-1/32	1-9/16	2-1/32	1-9/16	2-3/32	1-7/16	2-5/64	1-7/16	2-3/32	1-5/16	2-3/32
21	1-3/4	2-5/32	1-11/16	2-5/32	1-11/16	2-7/32	1-9/16	2-13/64	1-9/16	2-7/32	1-7/16	2-7/32
22	1-7/8	2-9/32	1-13/16	2-9/32	1-13/16	2-11/32	1-11/16	2-21/64	1-11/16	2-11/32	1-9/16	2-11/32
23	2	2-13/32	1-15/16	2-13/32	1-15/16	2-15/32	1-13/16	2-29/64	1-13/16	2-15/32	1-11/16	2-15/32
24	2-1/8	2-17/32	2-1/16	2-17/32	2-1/16	2-19/32	1-15/16	2-37/64	2-1/16	2-19/32	1-13/16	2-19/32
25	2-1/4	2-21/32	2-3/16	2-21/32	2-3/16	2-23/32	2-1/16	2-45/64	2-1/16	2-23/32	1-15/16	2-23/32
26	2-3/8	2-25/32	2-5/16	2-25/32	2-5/16	2-27/32	2-3/16	2-53/64	2-3/16	2-27/32	2-1/16	2-27/32
27	2-1/2	2-29/32	2-7/16	2-29/32	2-7/16	2-31/32	2-5/16	2-61/64	2-5/16	2-31/32	2-3/16	2-31/32
30	2-5/8	3-1/32	2-9/16	3-1/32	2-9/16	3-3/32	2-7/16	3-5/64	2-7/16	3-3/32	2-5/16	3-3/32
31	2-3/4	3-5/32	2-11/16	3-5/32	2-11/16	3-7/32	2-9/16	3-13/64	2-9/16	3-7/32	2-7/16	3-7/32
32	2-7/8	3-9/32	2-13/16	3-9/32	2-13/16	3-11/32	2-11/16	3-21/64	2-11/16	3-11/32	2-9/16	3-11/32
33	3	3-13/32	2-15/16	3-13/32	2-15/16	3-15/32	2-13/16	3-29/64	2-13/16	3-15/32	2-11/16	3-15/32
34	3-1/8	3-17/32	3-1/16	3-17/32	3-1/16	3-19/32	2-15/16	3-37/64	2-15/16	3-19/32	2-13/16	3-19/32
35	3-1/4	3-21/32	3-3/16	3-21/32	3-3/16	3-23/32	3-1/16	3-45/64	3-1/16	3-23/32	2-15/16	3-23/32
36	3-3/8	3-25/32	3-5/16	3-25/32	3-5/16	3-27/32	3-3/16	3-53/64	3-3/16	3-27/32	3-1/16	3-27/32
37	3-1/2	3-29/32	3-7/16	3-29/32	3-7/16	3-31/32	3-5/16	3-61/64	3-5/16	3-31/32	3-3/16	3-31/32
40	3-5/8	4-1/32	3-9/16	4-1/32	3-9/16	4-3/32	3-7/16	4-5/64	3-7/16	4-3/32	3-5/16	4-3/32

AN21 – AN36 CLEVIS BOLT

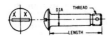

PART NUMBER EXAMPLES FOR CLEVIS BOLT
HAVING A #10-32 DIAMETER AND NOMINAL
LENGTH OF 15/16".
AN23-15   (HAS COTTER PIN HOLE)
AN23-15A (NO COTTER PIN HOLE)

The clevis bolt is used for shear loads only and requires a shear nut AN320 (for use with cotter pin) or AN364 (MS20364) self-locking nut. Nominal sizes, grip length and tolerances are shown. Only AN23, 24 and 25 are shown. Other diameters are indicated by AN number. For example, AN28 is 8/16 or 1/2″ diameter. Lengths are in sixteenths of an inch, -18 is 18 sixteenths or 1 1/8″ long.

DASH NO.	AN23 GRIP	LENGTH	AN24 GRIP	LENGTH	AN25 GRIP	LENGTH
8	3/16	17/32	3/16	17/32		
9	1/4	19/32	1/4	19/32	1/4	39/64
10	5/16	21/32	5/16	21/32	5/16	43/64
11	3/8	23/32	3/8	23/32	3/8	47/64
12	7/16	25/32	7/16	25/32	7/16	51/64
13	1/2	27/32	1/2	27/32	1/2	55/64
14	9/16	29/32	9/16	29/32	9/16	59/64
15	5/8	31/32	5/8	31/32	5/8	63/64
16	11/16	1- 1/32	11/16	1- 1/32	11/16	1- 3/64
17	3/4	1- 3/32	3/4	1- 3/32	3/4	1- 7/64
18	13/16	1- 5/32	13/16	1- 5/32	13/16	1-11/64
19	7/8	1- 7/32	7/8	1- 7/32	7/8	1-15/64
20	15/16	1- 9/32	15/16	1- 9/32	15/16	1-19/64
21	1	1-11/32	1	1-11/32	1	1-23/64
22	1- 1/16	1-13/32	1- 1/16	1-13/32	1- 1/16	1-27/64
23	1- 1/8	1-15/32	1- 1/8	1-15/32	1- 1/8	1-31/64
24	1- 3/16	1-17/32	1- 3/16	1-17/32	1- 3/16	1-35/64
25	1- 1/4	1-19/32	1- 1/4	1-19/32	1- 1/4	1-39/64
26	1- 5/16	1-21/32	1- 5/16	1-21/32	1- 5/16	1-43/64
27	1- 3/8	1-23/32	1- 3/8	1-23/32	1- 3/8	1-47/64
28	1- 7/16	1-25/32	1- 7/16	1-25/32	1- 7/16	1-51/64
29	1- 1/2	1-27/32	1- 1/2	1-27/32	1- 1/2	1-55/64
30	1- 9/16	1-29/32	1- 9/16	1-29/32	1- 9/16	1-59/64
31	1- 5/8	1-31/32	1- 5/8	1-31/32	1- 5/8	1-63/64
32	1-11/16	2- 1/32	1-11/16	2- 1/32	1-11/16	2- 3/64
34	1-13/16	2- 5/32	1-13/16	2- 5/32	1-13/16	2-11/64
36	1-15/16	2- 9/32	1-15/16	2- 9/32	1-15/16	2-19/64
38	2- 1/16	2-13/32	2- 1/16	2-13/32	2- 1/16	2-27/64
40	2- 3/16	2-17/32	2- 3/16	2-17/32	2- 3/16	2-35/64
42	2- 5/16	2-21/32	2- 5/16	2-21/32	2- 5/16	2-43/64
44	2- 7/16	2-25/32	2- 7/16	2-25/32	2- 7/16	2-51/64
46	2- 9/16	2-29/32	2- 9/16	2-29/32	2- 9/16	2-59/64
48	2-11/16	3- 1/32	2-11/16	3- 1/32	2-11/16	3- 3/64
50	2-13/16	3- 5/32	2-13/16	3- 5/32	2-13/16	3-11/64
52	2-15/16	3- 9/32	2-15/16	3- 9/32	2-15/16	3-19/64
54	3- 1/16	3-13/32	3- 1/16	3-13/32	3- 1/16	3-27/64
56	3- 3/16	3-17/32	3- 3/16	3-17/32	3- 3/16	3-35/64
58	3- 5/16	3-21/32	3- 5/16	3-21/32	3- 5/16	3-43/64
60	3- 7/16	3-25/32	3- 7/16	3-25/32	3- 7/16	3-51/64
62	3- 9/16	3-29/32	3- 9/16	3-29/32	3- 9/16	3-59/64
64	3-11/16	4- 1/32	3-11/16	4- 1/32	3-11/16	4- 3/64
66			3-13/16	4- 5/32		
68			3-15/16	4- 9/32		
70			4- 1/16	4-13/32		
72			4- 3/16	4-17/32		

AN23	AN24	AN25
#10	1/4	5/16
-32	-28	-24

AN DASH NUMBER	NOMINAL LENGTH
-8	1/2
-9	9/16
-10	5/8
-11	11/16
-12	3/4
-13	13/16
-14	7/8
-15	15/16
-16	1
-17	1-1/16
-18	1-1/8
-19	1-3/16
-20	1-1/4
-21	1-5/16
-22	1-3/8
-23	1-7/16
-24	1-1/2
-25	1-9/16
-26	1-5/8
-27	1-11/16
-28	1-3/4
-29	1-13/16
-30	1-7/8
-31	1-15/16
-32	2

AN42 – AN49 EYE BOLT

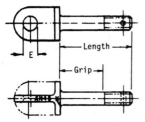

AN#	SIZE	E MIN	E MAX	Pin SIZE
AN42B	10-32	.190	.192	3/16
AN43B	1/4-28	.190	.192	3/16
AN44	5/16-24	.250	.253	1/4
AN45	5/16-24	.313	.316	5/16
AN46	3/8-24	.375	.378	3/8
AN47	7/16-20	.375	.378	3/8
AN48	1/2-20	.438	.441	7/16
AN49	9/16-18	.500	.503	1/2

Dash numbers for grip and length are the same as those for aircraft bolts AN3 – AN20 of the same body diameter. Example: AN43-12 is eye bolt, 1/4 in. diameter, 3/16 eye and 1 1/4 in. long (add A for absence of hole).

AN392 – AN406 (MS20392) CLEVIS PIN

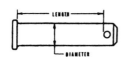

DIA.	AN PART NO.	MS20392 BASIC NO.	DASH NO. RANGE
1/8	AN392	-1C	-7 thru -67
3/16	AN393	-2C	-7 thru -95
1/4	AN394	-3C	-11 thru -97
5/16	AN395	-4C	-11 thru -97
3/8	AN396	-5C	-15 thru -127
7/16	AN397	-6C	-15 thru -127
1/2	AN398	-7C	-15 thru -127
9/16	AN399	-8C	-15 thru -127
5/8	AN400	-9C	-15 thru -127
3/4	AN402	-10C	-15 thru -127
7/8	AN404	-11C	-19 thru -137
1"	AN406	-12C	-19 thru -137

DASH NUMBERS ARE THE GRIP LENGTH AS
EXPRESSED IN <u>ODD</u> 1/32'S OF AN INCH <u>ONLY</u>.

Example: AN395-41 is a 5/16" diameter pin with an effective length of 19/32". Equivalent MS number is MS20392-4C41.

1/8 DIAMETER			3/16 DIAMETER			1/4 DIAMETER		
AN392 DASH NO.	MS20392 DASH NO.	LENGTH	AN393 DASH NO.	MS20392 DASH NO.	LENGTH	AN394 DASH NO.	MS20392 DASH NO.	LENGTH
-7	1C7	7/32	-7	2C7	7/32	-11	3C11	11/32
-9	1C9	9/32	-9	2C9	9/32	-13	3C13	13/32
-11	1C11	11/32	-11	2C11	11/32	-15	3C15	15/32
-13	1C13	13/32	-13	2C13	13/32	-17	3C17	17/32
-15	1C15	15/32	-15	2C15	15/32	-19	3C19	19/32
-17	1C17	17/32	-17	2C17	17/32	-21	3C21	21/32
-19	1C19	19/32	-19	2C19	19/32	-23	3C23	23/32
-21	1C21	21/32	-21	2C21	21/32	-25	3C25	25/32
-23	1C23	23/32	-23	2C23	23/32	-27	3C27	27/32
-25	1C25	25/32	-25	2C25	25/32	-29	3C29	29/32
-27	1C27	27/32	-27	2C27	27/32	-31	3C31	31/32
-29	1C29	29/32	-29	2C29	29/32	-33	3C33	1-1/32
-31	1C31	31/32	-31	2C31	31/32	-35	3C35	1-3/32
-33	1C33	1-1/32	-33	2C33	1-1/32	-37	3C37	1-5/32
-35	1C35	1-3/32	-35	2C35	1-3/32	-39	3C39	1-7/32
-37	1C37	1-5/32	-37	2C37	1-5/32	-41	3C41	1-9/32
-39	1C39	1-7/32	-39	2C39	1-7/32	-43	3C43	1-11/32
-41	1C41	1-9/32	-41	2C41	1-9/32	-45	3C45	1-13/32
-43	1C43	1-11/32	-43	2C43	1-11/32	-47	3C47	1-15/32
-45	1C45	1-13/32	-45	2C45	1-13/32	-49	3C49	1-17/32
-47	1C47	1-15/32	-47	2C47	1-15/32	-51	3C51	1-19/32
-49	1C49	1-17/32	-49	2C49	1-17/32	-53	3C53	1-21/32
-51	1C51	1-19/32	-51	2C51	1-19/32	-55	3C55	1-23/32
-53	1C53	1-21/32	-53	2C53	1-21/32	-57	3C57	1-25/32
-55	1C55	1-23/32	-55	2C55	1-23/32	-59	3C59	1-27/32

MISCELLANEOUS NUTS

DASH NO.	SIZE
-3	#10-32
-4	1/4-28
-5	5/16-24
-6	3/8-24
-7	7/16-20
-8	1/2-20
-9	9/16-18
-10	5/8-18
-12	3/4-16
-14	7/8-14
-16	1-14

AN310—CASTLE   **AN315—PLAIN**   **AN316—CHECK**

AN320—SHEAR   **AN360 – ENGINE**

Steel nuts are cadmium plated per specification QQ-P-416.
Example: AN310-5 is castle nut made of steel and fits a 5/16 AN bolt.

CADMIUM PLATED STEEL LOCKNUTS, Nylon Insert

AN364   MS20364 (THIN)
TO 250° F.

CADMIUM PLATED STEEL

AN365   MS20365 (REGULAR)
TO 250° F.

CADMIUM PLATED STEEL

DASH NO.	SIZE
-440	#4-40
-632	#6-32
-832	#8-32
-1032	#10-32
-428	1/4-28
-524	5/16-24
-624	3/8-24
-720	7/16-20
-820	1/2-20
-918	9/16-18
-1018	5/8-18

Example: MS20364-624 is self-locking thin steel nut for 3/8″ bolt, 3/8-24 thread.

AN960 – FLAT WASHER

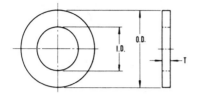

SCREW OR BOLT SIZE	REGULAR			
	DASH NO.	T DIM.	I.D.	O.D.
#2	-2	.032	.099	.250
#3	-3	.032	.105	.250
#4	-4	.032	.125	.312
#6	-6	.032	.149	.375
#8	-8	.032	.174	.375
#10	-10	.063	.203	.438
1/4	-416	.063	.265	.500
5/16	-516	.063	.328	.562
3/8	-616	.063	.390	.625
7/16	-716	.063	.453	.750
1/2	-816	.063	.515	.875
9/16	-916	.063	.578	1.062
5/8	-1016	.063	.640	1.188
3/4	-1216	.090	.765	1.312
7/8	-1416	.090	.890	1.500
1"	-1616	.090	1.015	1.750

AN960   - CADMIUM PLATED CARBON STEEL
AN960A - ALUMINUM (UNTREATED)
          (NOT READILY AVAILABLE, USE AN960D)
AN960B - BRASS
AN960C - STAINLESS STEEL
AN960D - ALUMINUM ALLOY, CONDITION T3 OR T4
AN960PD - ALUMINUM ALLOY, ANODIZED

AN380 (MS24665) – COTTER PIN

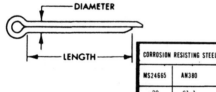

DASH NO.	DIAMETER AND THREAD	COTTER PINS FOR AN310 & AN320
-3	#10-32	AN380-2-1
-4	1/4-28	AN380-2-2
-5	5/16-24	AN380-2-2
-6	3/8-24	AN380-3-3
-7	7/16-20	AN380-3-3
-8	1/2-20	AN380-3-3
-9	9/16-18	AN380-4-4
-10	5/8-18	AN380-4-4
-12	3/4-16	AN380-4-5

CORROSION RESISTING STEEL		DIAMETER & LENGTH	CADMIUM PLATED STEEL	
MS24665	AN380		MS24665	AN380
-20	C1-1	1/32 x 3/8	-3	-1-1
-22	C1-2	1/32 x 1/2	-5	-1-2
-24	C1-3	1/32 x 3/4	-7	-1-3
-26	C1-4	1/32 x 1	-9	-1-4
-149	C2-1	1/16 x 3/8	-130	-2-1
-151	C2-2	1/16 x 1/2	-132	-2-2
-153	C2-3	1/16 x 3/4	-134	-2-3
-155	C2-4	1/16 x 1	-136	-2-4
-157	C2-5	1/16 x 1-1/4	-138	-2-5
-159	C2-6	1/16 x 1-1/2	-140	-2-6
-161	C2-7	1/16 x 1-3/4	-142	-2-7
-162	C2-8	1/16 x 2	-143	-2-8
-229		5/64 x 3/4		
-231		5/64 x 1		
-298	C3-2	3/32 x 1/2	-281	-3-2
-300	C3-3	3/32 x 3/4	-283	-3-3
-302	C3-4	3/32 x 1	-285	-3-4
-304	C3-5	3/32 x 1-1/4	-287	-3-5
-306	C3-6	3/32 x 1-1/2	-289	-3-6
-308	C3-7	3/32 x 1-3/4	-291	-3-7
-309	C3-8	3/32 x 2	-292	-3-8
-366	C4-2	1/8 x 1/2	-349	-4-2
-368	C4-3	1/8 x 3/4	-351	-4-3
-370	C4-4	1/8 x 1	-353	-4-4
-374	C4-6	1/8 x 1-1/2	-357	-4-6
-377	C4-8	1/8 x 2	-360	-4-8
-379	C4-10	1/8 x 2-1/2	-362	-4-10
		5/32 x 1/2	-419	-5-4
		5/32 x 1-1/2	-423	-5-6
	C5-9	5/32 x 2-1/4	-427	-5-9

MACHINE SCREWS

AN500A AND AN501A
MS35265 AND MS35266

DRILLED FILLISTER HEAD
SCREWS
CARBON STEEL
CADMIUM PLATED

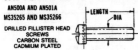

AN505   MS35190
AN510   MS35191
82°
FLAT HEAD

AN500A DASH	MS35265 DASH	THREAD	LENGTH
4-4	-13	#4-40	1/4
4-5	-14		5/16
4-6	-15		3/8
4-8	-17		1/2
6-4	-26	#6-32	1/4
6-5	-27		5/16
6-6	-28		3/8
6-8	-30		1/2
6-10	-31		5/8
6-12	-32		3/4
8-4	-41	#8-32	1/4
8-5	-42		5/16
8-6	-43		3/8
8-8	-45		1/2
8-10	-46		5/8
8-12	-47		3/4
8-14	-48		7/8
8-16	-49		1
10-4	-59	#10-24	1/4
10-6	-61		3/8
10-8	-63		1/2
10-10	-64		5/8
10-12	-65		3/4
10-14	-66		7/8
10-16	-67		1
416-8	-79	1/4-20	1/2
416-10	-80		5/8

AN501A DASH	MS35266 DASH	THREAD	LENGTH
10-4	-59	#10-32	1/4
10-5	-60		5/16
10-6	-61		3/8
10-8	-63		1/2
10-10	-64		5/8
10-12	-65		3/4
10-16	-67		1
416-10	-80	1/4-28	5/8

AN505 DASH	MS35190 DASH	THREAD	LENGTH
-4R4	-221	#4-40	1/4
-4R6	-223		3/8
-4R8	-225		1/2
-4R10	-227		3/4
-6R4	-234	#6-32	1/4
-6R6	-236		3/8
-6R8	-238		1/2
-6R10	-239		5/8
-6R12	-240		3/4
-6R14	-241		7/8
-6R16	-242		1
-8R4		#8-32	1/4
-8R6	-251		3/8
-8R8	-253		1/2
-8R10	-254		5/8
-8R12	-255		3/4
-8R16	-257		1
-8R20	-259		1-1/4
-8R24	-261		1-1/2

AN510 DASH	MS35191 DASH	THREAD	LENGTH
-10R4		#10-32	1/4
-10R6			3/8
-10R8			1/2
-10R10			5/8
-10R12			3/4
-10R14			7/8
-10R16			1

Example: AN500A-10-14
(MS35265-66) is fillister head screw,
10-24 thread and 7/8 in. long, drilled
head.

Example: AN505-8R10 (MS35191-254) is flat, recessed head, 8-32 thread
screw, 5/8 in. long.

MACHINE SCREWS

AN507 MS24693
100°
FLAT HEAD
CADMIUM PLATED CARBON STEEL

AN509 MS24694
100°
FLAT HEAD
STRUCTURAL

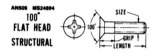

AN507 DASH	MS24693 DASH	THREAD	LENGTH
440R4	S2		1/4
440R5	S3		5/16
440R6	S4		3/8
440R8	S6	#4-40	1/2
440R10	S7		5/8
440R12	S8		3/4
440R14	S9		7/8
440R16	S10		1
632R4	S24		1/4
632R5	S25		5/16
632R6	S26		3/8
632R7	S27		7/16
632R8	S28		1/2
632R10	S29	#6-32	5/8
632R12	S30		3/4
632R14	S31		7/8
632R16	S32		1
632R20	S34		1-1/4
632R24	S36		1-1/2
832R4	S46		1/4
832R5	S47		5/16
832R6	S48		3/8
832R7	S49		7/16
832R8	S50		1/2
832R10	S51	#8-32	5/8
832R12	S52		3/4
832R14	S53		7/8
832R16	S54		1
832R20	S56		1-1/4
832R24	S58		1-1/2
1032R4	S268		1/4
1032R5	S269		5/16
1032R6	S270		3/8
1032R7	S271		7/16
1032R8	S272		1/2
1032R10	S273	#10-32	5/8
1032R12	S274		3/4
1032R14	S275		7/8
1032R16	S276		1
1032R20	S278		1-1/4
1032R24	S280		1-1/2

AN509 DASH	MS24694 DASH	SIZE	GRIP/LENGTH
8R5	S2		.093 - .343
8R6	S3		.093 - .406
8R7	S4		.093 - .468
8R8	S5		.093 - .531
8R9	S6		.156 - .593
8R10	S7		.218 - .656
8R11	S8	#8-32	.281 - .718
8R12	S9		.343 - .781
8R13	S10		.406 - .843
8R14	S11		.468 - .906
8R15	S12		.531 - .968
8R16	S13		.593 - 1.031
10R6	S48		.109 - .406
10R7	S49		.109 - .468
10R8	S50		.109 - .531
10R9	S51		.109 - .593
10R10	S52		.187 - .656
10R11	S53		.250 - .718
10R12	S54		.312 - .781
10R13	S55	#10-32	.375 - .843
10R14	S56		.437 - .906
10R15	S57		.500 - .968
10R16	S58		.562 - 1.031
10R17	S59		.625 - 1.093
10R18	S60		.687 - 1.156
10R19	S61		.750 - 1.218
10R20	S62		.812 - 1.281
416R7	S94		.140 - .468
416R8	S95		.140 - .531
416R9	S96		.140 - .593
416R10	S97		.140 - .656
416R11	S98		.187 - .718
416R12	S99		.250 - .781
416R13	S100	1/4-28	.312 - .843
416R14	S101		.375 - .906
416R15	S102		.437 - .968
416R16	S103		.500 - 1.031
416R17	S104		.562 - 1.093
416R18	S105		.652 - 1.156
416R19	S106		.687 - 1.218
416R20	S107		.750 - 1.281

Example: AN507-832R10 (MS24693-551) is flat, recessed head, 8-32 thread screw, 5/8 in. long.

Example: AN509-10R16 (MS24694-558) is flat, recessed head, 10-32 thread, structural screw, nominal length, 1 in. and 9/16 in. nominal grip length.

MACHINE SCREWS

AN526 TRUSS HEAD

DASH NO.	THREAD	LENGTH
632R4		1/4
632R5		5/16
632R6		3/8
632R7		7/16
632R8		1/2
632R9	#6-32	9/16
632R10		5/8
632R12		3/4
632R14		7/8
632R16		1
632R18		1-1/8
632R20		1-1/4
632R24		1-1/2
632R28		1-3/4
632R32		2
832R4		1/4
832R5		5/16
832R6		3/8
832R7		7/16
832R8		1/2
832R9	#8-32	9/16
832R10		5/8
832R12		3/4
832R14		7/8
832R16		1
832R18		1-1/8
832R20		1-1/4
832R24		1-1/2
832R28		1-3/4
832R32		2
1032R4		1/4
1032R5		5/16
1032R6		3/8
1032R7		7/16
1032R8		1/2
1032R9	#10-32	9/16
1032R10		5/8
1032R12		3/4
1032R14		7/8
1032R16		1
1032R18		1-1/8
1032R20		1-1/4
1032R24		1-1/2
1032R28		1-3/4
1032R32		2

MS27039

PAN HEAD
MACHINE SCREW
STRUCTURAL
CROSS RECESSED

DASH NO.	THREAD	LENGTH	GRIP
0804		.281	.032
0805		.344	.032
0806		.406	.032
0807		.469	.032
0808		.531	.094
0809		.594	.156
0810	#8-32	.656	.219
0811		.719	.281
0812		.781	.344
0813		.844	.406
0814		.906	.469
0815		.969	.531
0816		1.031	.594
0818		1.156	.719
0820		1.281	.844
0821		1.344	.906
1-06		.406	.032
1-07		.469	.032
1-08		.531	.062
1-09		.594	.125
1-10		.656	.188
1-11	#10-32	.719	.250
1-12		.781	.312
1-13		.844	.375
1-14		.906	.438
1-15		.969	.500
1-16		1.031	.563
4-12	1/4-28	.781	.250

Example: AN526-832R10 is truss head, recessed head screw, 8-32 thread and 5/8 in. long.

Example: MS27039-0816 is pan-head structural, recessed head, screw 8-32 thread, nominal length 1 in. and nominal grip length of 19/32 in.

SHEET-METAL SELF TAPPING SCREWS

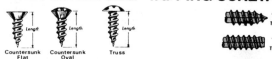

Countersunk Flat	Countersunk Oval	Truss	

"A" TYPE

"B" TYPE

TYPE "A" IS A COARSE-THREADED SCREW WITH A SHARP GIMLET POINT. TYPE "B" OR "Z" (USED WITH TINNERMAN SPEED NUTS) HAS FINER PITCHED THREADS AND IS BLUNT ENDED. A REFINEMENT OF BOTH IS TYPE "AB" THAT HAS THE "B" THREAD AND THE SHARP "A" POINT.

LENGTH
1/4
3/8
1/2
5/8
3/4
1-
1-1/4
1-1/2

SIZE	#4	#6	#8	#10

Phillips Recessed   **Slotted**

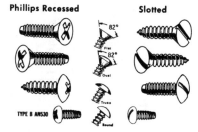

TYPE B AN530

NAS548 (MS21207)

NAS 548 (MS21207)
100° PHILLIPS FLAT HEAD
TYPE "B" TAPPING SCREW

NAS548 (MS21207)	DIAMETER 1st DASH NO.	#6 -6	#8 -8	#10 -10

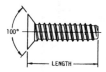

100°

LENGTH

2nd DASH NUMBER	LENGTH
-6	3/8
-8	1/2
-10	5/8
-12	3/4

Example: NAS548-8-8 is #8 Phillips, 100-degree flat-head type B, tapping screw, 1/2 in. long. (NAS548-8-8 is the same as #8 × 1/2, 100-degree flat-head tapping screw.)

TINNERMAN SPEED NUT
Flat Type

USE WITH TYPE B (BLUNT TAPER AT END) TAPPING SCREWS:

PART NUMBER	SCREW SIZE	A LENGTH	B WIDTH
A1776-4Z-1	4B	.500	.312
A1181-6Z-1	6B	.515	.312
A1777-6Z-1	6B	.625	.437
A1778-8Z-1	8B	.625	.437
A1779-10Z-1	10B	.875	.500

FOR USE WITH MACHINE SCREWS

PART NUMBER	SCREW SIZE
A105-440-1	4-40
A1322-632-1	6-32
A1322-832-1	8-32

DESIGN VARIATIONS AVAILABLE

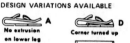

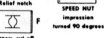

A No extrusion on lower leg

B Full extrusion on lower leg

C Straight upper leg

D Corner turned up

E Relief notch

F Corners cut off

H SPEED NUT impression turned 90 degrees

U Type

SELF-RETAINING "U" TYPE, PRESS EASILY INTO LOCKED-ON POSITION OVER PANEL EDGES OR IN CENTER PANEL LOCATIONS. THEY HOLD THEMSELVES IN A SCREW-RECEIVING POSITION AND ARE IDEALLY SUITED FOR BLIND ASSEMBLY OR HARD-TO-REACH LOCATIONS. IDEALLY SUITED WHERE FULL BEARING SURFACE ON THE LOWER LEG OF THE SPEED NUT IS REQUIRED.

PART NUMBER	SCREW SIZE	DESIGN	PANEL RANGE	LENGTH A	WIDTH B
A6187-4Z-1	4	CD	.025-.032	.375	.312
A1784-6Z-1	6	E	.025-.051	.640	.437
A1785-6Z-1	6	E	.025-.064	.843	.437
A6052-6Z-1	6	EH	.032-.040	.468	.500
A1274-8Z-1	8	DEH	.025-.032	.500	.500
A1348-8Z-1	8	AE	.025-.064	.750	.500
A1786-8Z-1	8	CEH	.040-.051	.531	.500
A1787-8Z-1	8	E	.025-.064	.843	.437
A1788-8Z-1	8	AE	.025-.064	.843	.437
A1789-8Z-1	8	E	.025-.051	.640	.437
A1932-8Z-1	8	BE	.032-.051	.593	.500
A1350-10Z-1	10	AE	.025-.064	.750	.500
A1758-10Z-1	10	E	.081-.094	.640	.437
A1787-10Z-1	10	E	.025-.064	.843	.437
A1791-10Z-1	10	EH	.040-.064	.625	.625
A1794-10Z-1	10	E	.032-.064	.640	.437
A9031-10Z-1	10	EH	.102-.125	.703	.625

SOLID RIVETS

MS20470 UNIVERSAL HEAD

MS20470A	MS20470AD
AN470A	AN470AD

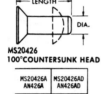

MS20426
100°COUNTERSUNK HEAD

MS20426A	MS20426AD
AN426A	AN426AD

The MS20426 and MS20470 types are the most widely used: manufactured to Mil-R-5674. These two types are available in most sizes in two materials: "hard" 2117 aluminum alloy (AD) and "soft" 1100 pure aluminum (A).

Example of part no.: MS20426A3-12 is $3/32''$ dia., $3/4''$ long, 100 degrees countersunk head "soft."

DASH NO.	DIA.	LENGTH
2-6	1/16	3/8
2-8		1/2
2-9		9/16
3-3	3/32	3/16
3-4		1/4
3-5		5/16
3-6		3/8
3-8		1/2
3-12		3/4
4-3	1/8	3/16
4-4		1/4
4-5		5/16
4-6		3/8
4-7		7/16
4-8		1/2
4-9		9/16
4-10		5/8
4-11		11/16
4-12		3/4
4-14		7/8
4-16		1
4-18		1-1/8
4-20		1-1/4
4-30		1-7/8
5-4	5/32	1/4
5-5		5/16
5-6		3/8
5-7		7/16
5-8		1/2
5-9		9/16
5-10		5/8
5-12		3/4
5-16		1
5-22		1-3/8
6-4	3/16	1/4
6-5		5/16
6-6		3/8
6-7		7/16
6-8		1/2
6-10		5/8
6-12		3/4
6-14		7/8

MS TURNBUCKLES (CLIP-LOCKING)

Clip-Locking Turnbuckles utilize two locking clips instead of lockwire for safetying. The turnbuckle barrel and terminals are slotted lengthwise to accommodate the locking clips. After the proper cable tension is reached the barrel slots are aligned with the terminal slots and the clips are inserted. The curved end of the locking clips expand and latch in the vertical slot in the center of the barrel.

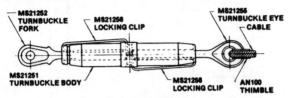

TYPICAL TURNBUCKLE ASSEMBLY

MS Standard Drawings for clip-locking turnbuckles supersede various AN Drawings for conventional (lockwire type) turnbuckle parts and NAS Drawings for clip-locking turnbuckle parts. Refer to the following cross reference tables for AN and NAS equivalents.

MS21251 TURNBUCKLE BARREL

Supersedes AN155 and NAS649 barrels. MS21251 items can replace AN155 items of like material and thread, but the AN155 items cannot replace the MS21251 items. MS21251 items are interchangeable with the NAS649 items of like material and thread. MS21251 barrels are available in brass (QQ-B-637, composition 2 or MIL-T-6945), steel (cadmium plated to QQ-P-416, type 2, class 3) or aluminum alloy (anodized to MIL-A-8725). The cross reference table shows equivalent items made of brass.

MS21251 DASH NO.	ROPE DIA.	THREAD SIZE	AN155 DASH NO	NAS649 DASH NO.	USES MS21256 CLIP DASH NO.
B2S	1/16	6-40	B8S	B8S	-1
B2L	1/16	6-40	B8L	B8L	-2
B3S	3/32	10-32	B16S	B16S	-1
B3L	3/32	10-32	B16L	B16L	-2
B5S	5/32	1/4-28	B32S	B32S	-1
B5L	5/32	1/4-28	B32L	B32L	-2
B6S	3/16	5/16-24	B46S	B46S	-1
B6L	3/16	5/16-24	B46L	B46L	-2
B8L	1/4	3/8-24	B80L	B80L	-2
B9L	9/32	7/16-20	B125L	B125L	-3
B10L	5/16	1/2-20	B175L	B175L	-3

TERMINALS

MS items can replace AN items of like thread except for the -22 and -61 sizes, but the AN items cannot replace the MS items. MS items are interchangeable with the NAS items of like thread except for the -22 and -61 sizes. These MS terminals are available only in steel cadmium plated to QQ-P-416, type 2, class 3. Available with right-hand (R) or left-hand (L) threads.

MS21252 TURNBUCKLE FORK supersedes AN161 and NAS645 forks.

MS21254 PIN EYE supersedes AN165 and NAS648 eyes.

MS21255 CABLE EYE supersedes AN170 and NAS 647 eyes.

MS21260 SWAGED STUD END supersedes AN669 studs.

MS21252 MS21254 MS21255 DASH NOS.		WIRE ROPE DIA.	THREAD SIZE	AN 161 AN165 AN170 DASH NOS.		NAS645 NAS648 NAS647 DASH NOS.	
RH THD	LH THD			RH THD	LH THD	RH THD	LH THD
-2RS	-2LS	1/16	6-40	-8RS	-8LS	-8RS	-8LS
-2RL*	-2LL*	1/16	6-40	—	—	—	—
-3RS	-3LS	3/32	10-32	-16RS	-16LS	-16RS	-16LS
-3RL	-3LL	3/32	10-32	-16RL	-16LL	-16RL	-16LL
-5RS	-5LS	5/32	1/4-28	-32RS	-32LS	-32RS	-32LS
-5RL	-5LL	5/32	1/4-28	-32RL	-32LL	-32RL	-32LL
-6RS	-6LS	3/16	5/16-24	-46RS	-46LS	-46RS	-46LS
-6RL	-6LL	3/16	5/16-24	-46RL	-46LL	-46RL	-46LL
-8RL	-8LL	1/4	3/8-24	-80RL	-80LL	-80RL	-80LL
-9RL	-9LL	9/32	7/16-20	-125RL	-125LL	-125RL	-125LL
-10RL	-10LL	5/16	1/2-20	-175RL	-175LL	-175RL	-175LL

*MS21254 and MS21255 eyes only; MS21252 fork not made in this size.

MS21256 TURNBUCKLE CLIP

Made of corrosion resistant steel wire, QQ-W-423, composition FS302, condition B. These are NOT interchangeable with the NAS651 clips. Available in 3 sizes: MS21256-1, -2 and -3. For applications, see the MS21251 Turnbuckle Barrel Cross Reference Chart.

MS21260 SWAGED STUD END

These clip-locking terminals are available in corrosion resistant steel and in cadmium plated carbon steel. MS21260 items can replace AN669 items of the same dash numbers, but the AN669 items cannot always replace the MS21260 items.

Example: The AN "equivalent" (the AN equivalent would not be clip-locking) for MS21260 L3RH would be AN669-L3RH. There would be no AN equivalent for a MS21260FL3RH, since AN669 terminals are not available in carbon steel.

PART NUMBER	THREAD	CABLE DIA.	DESCRIPTION
MS21255-3LS	10-32	3/32	Eye End (for cable)
-3RS	10-32	3/32	
MS21256-1	—	—	Clip (for short barrels)
-2	—	—	Clip (for long barrels)
MS21260-S2LH	6-40	1/16	
-S2RH	6-40	1/16	
-S3LH	10-32	3/32	
-S3RH	10-32	3/32	
-L3LH	10-32	3/32	End (for cable)
-L3RH	10-32	3/32	
-S4LH	¼-28	1/8	
-S4RH	¼-28	1/8	
-L4LH	¼-28	1/8	
-L4RH	¼-28	1/8	

PART NUMBER	THREAD	CABLE DIA.	DESCRIPTION
MS21251-B2S	6-40	1/16	
-B3S	10-32	3/32	
-B3L	10-32	3/32	Barrel (Body), Brass
-B5S	¼-28	5/32	
-B5L	¼-28	5/32	
MS21252-3LS	10-32	3/32	
-3RS	10-32	3/32	Fork (Clevis End)
-5RS	¼-28	5/32	
MS21254-2RS	6-40	1/16	
-3LS	10-32	3/32	
-3RS	10-32	3/32	Eye End (for pin)
-5LS	¼-28	5/32	
-5RS	¼-28	5/32	

AN TURNBUCKLE ASSEMBLIES

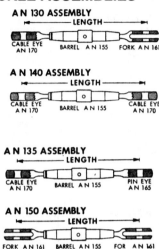

Turnbuckles consist of a brass barrel, and two steel ends, one having a right-handed thread and the other a left-handed thread. Types of turnbuckle ends are cable eye, pin eye, and fork. Turnbuckles illustrated on this page show four recommended assemblies. Turnbuckle barrels are made of brass: cable eyes, pin eyes, and forks of cadmium plated steel.

Example: AN155-8S (Barrel; length 2¼″) AN161-16RS (Fork; short, R.H. thread)

DASH NO.	LENGTH		STRENGTH	THREAD SIZE
	AN130	OTHERS		
8S	4-1/2	4-1/2	800	6-40
16S	4-1/2	4-1/2	1600	10-32
16L	8	8	1600	10-32
22S	4-17/32	4-1/2	2200	1/4-28
22L	8-1/32	8	2200	1/4-28
32S	4-19/32	4-1/2	3200	1/4-28
32L	8-7/64	8	3200	1/4-28

SWAGING TERMINALS

AN663C MS20663
BALL AND DOUBLE SHANK

DASH NUMBER	CABLE DIAMETER	FINISHED DIAMETER	
		BALL	SHANK
2	1/16	.190	.112
3	3/32	.250	.140
4	1/8	.312	.190
5	5/32	.375	.218
6	3/16	.437	.250

AN664C MS20664
BALL AND SHANK

DASH NUMBER	CABLE DIAMETER	FINISHED DIAMETER	
		BALL	SHANK
2	1/16	.190	.112
3	3/32	.250	.140
4	1/8	.312	.190
5	5/32	.375	.218
6	3/16	.437	.250

AN666   MS21259
STUD END

DASH NUMBER		CABLE DIAMETER	THREAD SIZE
RIGHT HAND	LEFT HAND		
2RH	2LH	1/16	#6-40
3RH	3LH	3/32	#10-32
4RH	4LH	1/8	1/4-28
5RH	5LH	5/32	1/4-28

AN667   MS20667
FORK END

DASH NUMBER	CABLE DIAMETER	PIN HOLE DIAMETER	SLOT WIDTH
2	1/16	.190	.093
3	3/32	.190	.108
4	1/8	.190	.195
5	5/32	.250	.202

AN668   MS20668
EYE END

DASH NUMBER	CABLE DIAMETER	PIN HOLE DIAMETER	BLADE WIDTH
2	1/16	.190	.088
3	3/32	.190	.103
4	1/8	.190	.190
5	5/32	.250	.197

(FOR SAFETY WIRE) **AN669   STUD END   MS21260** (SLOTTED FOR CLIP)

TURNBUCKLE END — SHORT

DASH NUMBER		CABLE DIAMETER	THREAD SIZE
RIGHT HAND	LEFT HAND		
S2RH	S2LH	1/16	6-40
S3RH	S3LH	3/32	10-32
S4RH	S4LH	1/8	1/4-28

TURNBUCKLE END — LONG

DASH NUMBER		CABLE DIAMETER	THREAD SIZE
RIGHT HAND	LEFT HAND		
L2RH	L2LH	1/16	6-40
L3RH	L3LH	3/32	10-32
L4RH	L4LH	1/8	1/4-28

PLUMBING FITTINGS AN774-AN932

Material:

Aluminum alloy............................(code D)
Steel..(code, absence of letter)
Brass..(code B)
Aluminum bronze........................(code Z—for AN819 sleeve)

Size: The dash number following the AN number indicates the size of the tubing (or hose) for which the fitting is made, in 16ths of an inch. This size measures the O. D. of tubing and the I. D. of hose. Fittings having pipe threads are coded by a dash number, indicating the pipe size in 8ths of an inch. The material code letter, as noted above, follows the dash number.

Example: AN822-5-4D is an aluminum 90° elbow for 5/16 in. tubing and 1/4 in. pipe thread.

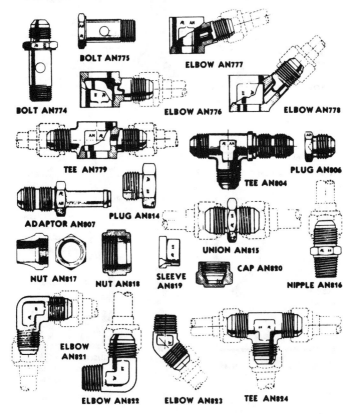

PLUMBING FITTINGS
(Continued from page 187.)

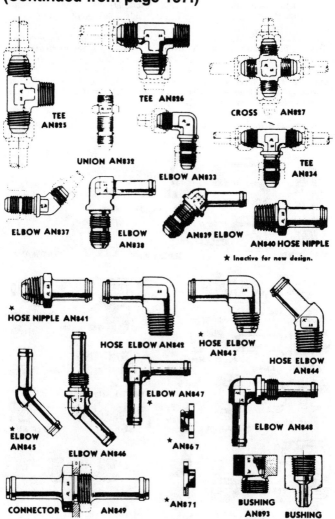

TEE AN825

TEE AN826

CROSS   AN827

UNION AN832

ELBOW AN833

TEE AN834

ELBOW AN837

ELBOW AN838

AN839 ELBOW

AN840 HOSE NIPPLE

★ Inactive for new design.

HOSE NIPPLE AN841

HOSE ELBOW AN842

HOSE ELBOW AN843

HOSE ELBOW AN844

ELBOW AN845

ELBOW AN846

ELBOW AN847

AN867

ELBOW AN848

CONNECTOR   AN849

AN871

BUSHING AN893

BUSHING AN894

PLUMBING FITTINGS
(Continued from page 188.)

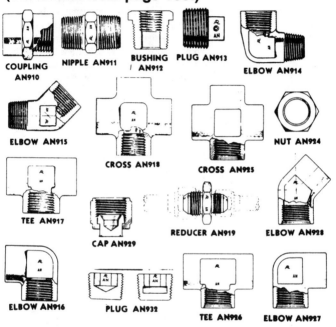

COUPLING AN910

NIPPLE AN911

BUSHING AN912

PLUG AN913

ELBOW AN914

ELBOW AN915

CROSS AN918

CROSS AN925

NUT AN924

TEE AN917

CAP AN929

REDUCER AN919

ELBOW AN928

ELBOW AN916

PLUG AN932

TEE AN926

ELBOW AN927

ADDITIONAL STANDARD PARTS (PATENTED)

The following pages illustrate a few fastener types widely used on high performance aircraft. These fasteners are designed and manufactured by various companies, are patented, and are generally known by their trade names.

It is emphasized that the following pages are in no way a complete list of patented fasteners available. Representative examples only are shown for illustrative purposes. All these fasteners require special installation tools and procedures. Installation manuals are available from the manufacturers.

CONVERSION TABLE ─────────────────

NAS NUMBERS TO CHERRY RIVET NUMBERS
(A COMPLETE CONVERSION TABLE OF CHERRY RIVET NUMBERS IS AVAILABLE UPON REQUEST)

BULBED CHERRYLOCK® RIVETS

HEAD STYLE	NAS NUMBER	CHERRY NUMBER	RIVET MATERIAL	STEM MATERIAL
UNIVERSAL HEAD	NAS 1738B 1738E 1738M 1738MW 1738C 1738CW	CR2249 2239 2539 2539P 2839 2839CW	5056 Aluminum 5056 Aluminum Monel Monel, Cad. Plt'd. Inconel 600 Inconel 600, Cad. Plt'd.	Alloy Steel, Cad. Plt'd. Inconel 600 Inconel 600 Inconel 600 A286 CRES A286 CRES
COUNTERSUNK HEAD (MS20426)	NAS 1739B 1739E 1739M 1739MW 1739C 1739CW	CR2248 2238 2538 2538P 2838 2838CW	5056 Aluminum 5056 Aluminum Monel Monel, Cad. Plt'd. Inconel 600 Inconel 600, Cad. Plt'd.	Alloy Steel, Cad. Plt'd. Inconel 600 Inconel 600 Inconel 600 A286 CRES A286 CRES
UNISINK HEAD	– – – –	CR2235 2245 2545 2845	5056 Aluminum 5056 Aluminum Monel Inconel 600	Inconel 600 Alloy Steel, Cad. Plt'd. Inconel 600 A286 CRES
COUNTERSUNK HEAD (156°)	– –	CR2540 2840	Monel Inconel 600	Inconel 600 A286 CRES

BULBED CHERRYLOCK° RIVETS

NAS 1738 UNIVERSAL HEAD

PROCUREMENT SPECIFICATION NAS 1740 IS APPLICABLE TO NAS 1738 RIVETS.

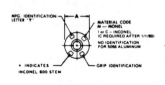

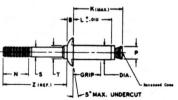

OPTIONAL CONFIGURATION
FOR A286 AND INCONEL STEMS

DIA., DASH NO.	-4	-5	-6
DIA. +.003/-.001	.140	.173	.201
A +.010	.250	.312	.375
B +.010/-.000	.054	.067	.080
N (MIN.)	.375	.375	.375
S +.006/-.003	.090	.112	.132
T (REF.)	.119	.140	.174
P (MAX.)	.143	.176	.205
BK ALUMINUM	.30	.33	.37
BK MONEL & INCONEL	.33	.37	.41
Z (REF)	1.65	1.63	1.65

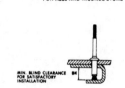

MIN. BLIND CLEARANCE BK
FOR SATISFACTORY
INSTALLATION

GRIP LIMITS 1/16" RANGE		RIVET GROUP	1/8 DIAMETER					5/32 DIAMETER					3/16 DIAMETER				
MIN.	MAX.		DASH NO.	ALUMINUM		MONEL & INCONEL		DASH NO.	ALUMINUM		MONEL & INCONEL		DASH NO.	ALUMINUM		MONEL & INCONEL	
				L	K	L	K		L	K	L	K		L	K	L	K
(1)	.062	A	4-1	.183	.32	.203	.34	5-1	.205	.35	.236	.39	6-1	.233	.39	.264	.43
.063	.125		4-2	.242	.38	.265	.40	5-2	.265	.41	.298	.45	6-2	.293	.45	.326	.49
.126	.187		4-3	.306	.45	.328	.47	5-3	.329	.47	.360	.51	6-3	.357	.52	.389	.55
.188	.250		4-4	.370	.51	.390	.53	5-4	.393	.54	.423	.58	6-4	.421	.58	.452	.61
.251	.312		4-5	.434	.58	.453	.59	5-5	.457	.60	.485	.64	6-5	.485	.65	.514	.68
.313	.375		4-6	.498	.64	.515	.65	5-6	.521	.67	.548	.70	6-6	.549	.71	.577	.74
.376	.437		4-7	.562	.71	.578	.72	5-7	.585	.73	.610	.76	6-7	.613	.78	.639	.80
.438	.500		4-8	.626	.77	.640	.78	5-8	.649	.80	.673	.83	6-8	.677	.84	.702	.86
.501	.562		4-9	.690	.84	.703	.84	5-9	.713	.86	.735	.89	6-9	.741	.91	.764	.93
.563	.625							5-10	.777	.93	.798	.95	6-10	.805	.97	.827	.99
.626	.687							5-11	.841	.99	.860	1.01	6-11	.869	1.04	.889	1.05
.688	.750												6-12	.933	1.10	.952	1.11

RIVET DIA.	MIN. GRIP
1/8	.020
5/32	.025
3/16	.030

RIVET GROUP REFERS TO SHIFT-POINT SETTING OF RIVETER.

hi-shear RIVET IDENTIFICATION CHART

PART NUMBER	IDENTIFICATION (HI-SHEAR CORPORATION) HEAD MARKING OR COLOR CODE	MATERIAL	PHYSICAL PROPERTIES ROOM TEMP	HEAD TYPE	TOLERANCES MINIMUM C'SK HEAD HEIGHT	SHANK DIAMETER	HI-SHEAR COLLAR TO ORDER	SUGGESTED MAXIMUM TEMP FOR USE	CHARACTERISTICS	NAS OR CUSTOMER PART NUMBER
NAS177	+	Alloy Steel	125,000-150,000 psi Tensile	Csk					Inactive.	
NAS178				Flat		0025	NAS179		See HS47, HS47PB and HS48, or NAS1054 and NAS1055.	
NAS179	Grey	2117-T4 Aluminum Alloy							Inactive. See HS15 or NAS528.	
NAS 528	Red	2024-T4 Aluminum Alloy							Hi-Shear Collar used in combination with 160,000-190,000 psi tensile Hi-Shear Rivet Pins. Same as HS15.	
NAS1806 thru NAS1816	NAS 1810 HV	6A1-4V Titanium Alloy	95,000 psi Shear Minimum	Flat		.0005	HS15		Chamfered lead style. Used in high performance aircraft where weight, shank and hole tolerances are critical.	
NAS1906 thru NAS1916	NAS 1910 HV	6A1-4V Titanium Alloy	95,000 psi Shear Minimum	Csk		0005	HS15		Chamfered lead style. Used in high performance aircraft where weight, shank and hole tolerances are critical.	
HS10	(·)	Alloy Steel	160,000-190,000 psi Tensile	Csk		0025	HS15		Stud Rivet Pin — fastens primary structure and provides for a means of attaching removable elements.	
HS15	Red	2024-T4 Aluminum Alloy						200°F	Hi-Shear Collar used in combination with 160,000-190,000 psi tensile Hi-Shear Rivet Pins.	NAS528
HS23 HS23A	*	7075-T6 Aluminum Alloy		Csk	.002	.001	HS24		Hi-Shear 100° head. Higher shear and tension allowables than DD Rivets. Small head permits countersinking in thin materials. "A" signifies sodium dichromate seal. For oversize, use HS39P or HS41P.	
HS24	Blue	2117-T4 Aluminum Alloy						200°F	Hi-Shear Collar used in combination with 7075-T6 aluminum alloy Hi-Shear Rivet Pins.	
HS25 HS25A	*	7075-T6 Aluminum Alloy		Csk	.002	.001	HS24		MS20426 style head. Higher shear and tension allowables than DD Rivets. "A" signifies sodium dichromate seal. For oversize, use HS25.32 or HS25.64.	

PART NUMBER	IDENTIFICATION HI-SHEAR CORPORATION HEAD MARKING OR COLOR CODE	MATERIAL	PHYSICAL PROPERTIES ROOM TEMP.	HEAD TYPE	TOLERANCES MINIMUM C'SK HEAD HEIGHT	SHANK DIAMETER	HI-SHEAR COLLAR TO ORDER	SUGGESTED MAXIMUM TEMP. FOR USE	CHARACTERISTICS	NAS OR CUSTOMER PART NUMBER
HS25.32 HS25.64	No Head Marking 1/32 – Red 1/64 – Blue	7075-T6 Aluminum Alloy		Csk	.002	.001	HS24		Oversizes for HS25.	
HS26 HS26A	(●*)	7075-T6 Aluminum Alloy		Flat		.001	HS24		Higher shear and tension allowables than DD Rivets. "A" signifies sodium dichromate seal. For oversize, use HS26.32 or HS26.64.	
HS26.32 HS26.64	No Head Marking 1/32 – Red 1/64 – Blue	7075-T6 Aluminum Alloy		Flat		.001	HS24		Oversizes for HS26.	
HS30	No Marking	Alloy Steel	160,000-180,000 psi Tensile	No Head		.0025	HS15 HS24 HS32		Dowel Pin grooved for collar on both ends. Lighter and stronger than Taper Pin. Precision fit molds to irregular surfaces (both sides). HS30 ground after plating: HS30P plated after grind.	
HS32	Silver (Cadmium Plate)	Low Carbon Steel							Hi-Shear Collar used in combination with 160,000-180,000 psi tensile Hi-Shear Rivets. Ferrous material applications.	
HS39P HS40P	(●·A)	Alloy Steel	160,000-180,000 psi Tensile	Csk Flat	.002	.0011	HS15		1/64 oversize Rivet Pin for HS23, HS26, HS47, HS48, HS51P, and HS52P. HS39PB and HS40PB – Type II plating.	
HS41P HS42P	(●·AI)	Alloy Steel	160,000-180,000 psi Tensile	Csk Flat	.002	.0011	HS15 or HS46		1/32 oversize Rivet Pin for HS23, HS26, HS47, HS48, HS51P, and HS52P. HS41PB and HS42PB – Type II plating.	
HS47 HS48	(●N)	Alloy Steel	160,000-180,000 psi Tensile	Csk Flat	.002	.0025	HS15		Chamfered lead style used in design where shank commercial tolerances are acceptable. For oversize use HS39P, HS40P, HS41P, or HS42P. HS47PB – Type II plating.	NAS1055 NAS1054
HS51P HS52P	(☐H)	Alloy Steel	160,000-180,000 psi Tensile	Csk Flat	.002	.0011	HS15		Chamfered lead style – plated after grind. Used in design where shank and hole tolerances are critical. For oversize use HS39P, HS40P, HS41P, or HS42P. HS51PB – Type II plating.	NAS525 NAS529
HS53	Red	2024-T4 Aluminum Alloy							Countersunk flanged Hi-Shear Collar used in double dimple applications. Used in combination with 160,000-180,000 psi tensile Hi-Shear Rivet Pins.	

PART NUMBER	IDENTIFICATION HI-SHEAR CORPORATION HEAD MARKING OR COLOR CODE	MATERIAL	PHYSICAL PROPERTIES ROOM TEMP.	HEAD TYPE	TOLERANCES MINIMUM		HI-SHEAR COLLAR TO ORDER	SUGGESTED MAXIMUM TEMP. FOR USE	CHARACTERISTICS	NAS OR CUSTOMER PART NUMBER
					C'SK HEAD HEIGHT	SHANK DIAMETER				
HS54	Blue	2117-T4 Aluminum Alloy							Countersunk flanged Hi-Shear Collar used in double dimple applications. Used in combination with 7075-T6 aluminum alloy Hi-Shear Rivet Pins.	
HS60	Natural	321 Stainless Steel						1600°F	Hi-Shear Collar for use in high temperature applications. Maximum temperature governed by conditions of application or use.	
HS60M	Black	"R" Monel or 400 Monel	RB 96 (Max.)					1000°F	Hi-Shear Collar used in high temperature applications to 900°F.	
HS61	61	Type 431 Stainless Steel	125,000 psi Shear Minimum	C'sk	.002		HS60 or HS60M	450°F	Used in high strength or temperature applications where shank and hole tolerances are critical. For oversize, use HS139, HS140, HS141, or HS142.	
HS62	62			Flat		.0005				
HS65	65	Type 305 Stainless Steel	125,000 psi Tensile	C'sk	.002		HS60 or HS60M		*Use HS60 Collars for non-magnetic application; HS60M for other applications.	
HS66	66			Flat		.0025				
HS67	67	Type 431 Stainless Steel	125,000 psi Shear Minimum	C'sk	.002		HS60 or HS60M	450°F	Used in high strength or temperature applications where shank commercial tolerances are acceptable. For oversize, use HS139, HS140, HS141, or HS142.	
HS68	68			Flat		.0025				
HS90	Natural	A-286 High Temp. Alloy					HS60M	1200°F	Hi-Shear Collar used in non-magnetic and high temperature applications.	
HS91	91	A-286 High Temp. Alloy	95,000 psi Shear Minimum	C'sk	.002		HS60M or HS90	1200°F (See Note)	Used in strength and temperature applications where shank and hole tolerances are critical. NOTE: For use in non-magnetic applications.	
HS92	92			Flat		.0005				
HS104	Natural	Inconel 600 per AMS5665						150°F	Used in combination with HS131 and HS132 Pins. For use at high temperature applications.	
HS106	No Head Marking	Alloy Steel	160,000-180,000 psi Tensile	Flat		Knurled Shank	HS24		Rivet Pin with threaded stud. Fastens primary structure and provides threaded stud to attach removal items.	

PART NUMBER	IDENTIFICATION (HI-SHEAR CORPORATION) HEAD MARKING OR COLOR CODE	MATERIAL	PHYSICAL PROPERTIES ROOM TEMP.	HEAD TYPE	TOLERANCES C'SK HEAD HEIGHT	TOLERANCES MINIMUM SHANK DIAMETER	HI-SHEAR COLLAR TO ORDER	SUGGESTED MAXIMUM TEMP FOR USE	CHARACTERISTICS	NAS OR CUSTOMER PART NUMBER
HS108	HS	Alloy Steel	160,000-180,000 psi Tensile	Protruding		.0025	HS15		Stud Rivet Pin. Fastens primary structure and provides stud to attach removable items.	
HS131	131	Inconel X-750	160,000 psi Tensile	Csk	.002	.0025	HS104	1500°F	Used at high temperature applications where commercial tolerances are acceptable.	
HS132	132	Inconel X-750	160,000 psi Tensile	Flat		.0025	HS104	1500°F		
HS139	139	Type 431 Stainless Steel	125,000 psi Shear Minimum	Csk	.002	.0005	HS60M	450°F	1/64 oversize for HS61, HS62, HS67 and HS68.	
HS140	140	Type 431 Stainless Steel	125,000 psi Shear Minimum	Flat		.0005	HS60M	450°F		
HS141	141	Type 431 Stainless Steel	125,000 psi Shear Minimum	Csk	.002	.0005	HS60M	450°F	1/32 oversize for HS61, HS62, HS67 and HS68.	
HS142	142	Type 431 Stainless Steel	125,000 psi Shear Minimum	Flat		.0005	HS60M	450°F		
HS149	H 149	6-4 Ti Alloy	160,000-180,000 psi Tensile	Csk	.002	.0005	HS15 HS167 HS234		Used in high performance aircraft where weight, material fatigue, shank and hole tolerances are critical.	NAS1806 NAS1906
HS150	H 150	6-4 Ti Alloy	160,000-180,000 psi Tensile	Flat		.0005				
HS154	154 P	Type H-11 Steel per AMS6485	156,000 psi Shear Min. Rc 50-55	Flat		.0025	HS90		Used in high temperature applications. "P" code – cadmium plate. "N" code – diffused nickel.	
HS155	155 N	Type H-11 Steel per AMS6485	156,000 psi Shear Min. Rc 50-55	Csk	.002	.0025	HS90			
HS159	H 159	A-286 High Temp. Alloy	160,000-180,000 psi Tensile	Csk	.002	001	HS60M		1/64 oversize for HS91 and HS92.	
HS160	H 160	A-286 High Temp. Alloy	160,000-180,000 psi Tensile	Flat		001	HS60M			
HS161	H 161	A-286 High Temp. Alloy	160,000-180,000 psi Tensile	Csk	.002	.0015	HS60M		1/32 oversize for HS91 and HS92.	
HS162	H 162	A-286 High Temp. Alloy	160,000-180,000 psi Tensile	Flat		.0015	HS60M			
HS167	Natural	Ti-50A Com. Pure Titanium						700°F	Hi-Shear Collar used in combination with HS149 and HS150 Pins and in non-magnetic applications.	
HS234	Violet	2219-T6 Aluminum Alloy						425°F	Hi-Shear Collar used at elevated temperatures.	

TRI-WING®

1. NAS STANDARDS AND SPECIFICATIONS
2. AIRLINE AND MANUFACTURERS APPROVAL
3. THREE-WING RECESSED DESIGN PERMITS EASY IDENTIFICATION
4. REDUCED WORK EFFORT BY THE OPERATOR RESULTS FROM LESS END THRUST
5. CLOSE-TOLERANCE CONTROL OF THE RECESS AND THE DRIVER BIT ACHIEVE OPTI-MUM PERFORMANCE
6. IMPROVED DRIVER BIT LIFE
7. PART NUMBERS ARE STAMPED ON THE FASTENER HEADS
8. DRIVER NUMBERS ARE STAMPED ON THE FASTENER HEADS
9. DRIVER BITS ARE NUMBERED WITH RECESS SIZE TO ELIMINATE MISMATCH PROBLEMS
10. POWER DRIVER OPERATIONS OF THE TRI-WING INSURE POSITIVE ENGAGEMENT – REDUCING THE CHANCE OF SURFACE DAMAGE TO THE ADJACENT STRUCTURE

TRI-WING® STANDARDS

NAS NUMBER	DIAMETER	HEAD STYLE	THREAD TYPE	MATERIAL	CLASSIFICATION	
NAS 4104-4116 NAS 4204-4216 NAS 4304-4316	.250 – 1.000"	100°	Long	Alloy Steel Cres Titanium	Bolt	
NAS 4400-4416 NAS 4500-4516 NAS 4600-4616	.112 – 1.000"	100°	Short	Alloy Steel Cres Titanium	Bolt	
NAS 4703-4716 NAS 4803-4816 NAS 4903-4916	.190 – 1.000"	100° Reduced	Short	Alloy Steel Cres Titanium	Bolt	
NAS 5000-5006 NAS 5100-5106 NAS 5200-5206	.112 – .375"	Pan	Short	Alloy Steel Cres Titanium	Screw	
NAS 5300-5306 NAS 5400-5406 NAS 5500-5506	.112 – .375"	Fillister	Full	Alloy Steel Cres Titanium	Screw	
NAS 5600-5606 NAS 5700-5706 NAS 5800-5806	.112 – .375"	100°	Full	Alloy Steel Cres Titanium	Screw	
NAS 5900-5903 NAS 6000-6003 NAS 6100-6103	.112 – .190"	Hex	Full	Alloy Steel Cres Titanium	Screw	

APPLICABLE SPECIFICATIONS

TRI-WING recess specification – NAS 4000   TRI-WING driver specification – NAS 4001
Alloy Steel process specification – NAS 4002   Cres process specification – NAS 4003
Titanium process specification – NAS 4004

TRI-WING® is a registered trademark of PHILLIPS SCREW COMPANY

STANDARDS COMMITTEE
FOR HI-LOK® PRODUCTS
2600 SKYPARK DRIVE, TORRANCE, CALIFORNIA 90509

						HI-LOK PIN
HI-LOK PIN PART NO.	PIN HEAD STYLE APPLICATION	MATERIAL	HEAT TREAT	SHANK DIA. TOL.	SUGGESTED MAXIMUM TEMP. FOR USE	GRIP VARIATION
HL10	Protruding —— Shear	6Al-4V Titanium	95,000 psi Shear Minimum	.0005 or .0010	750° F or Sub. to Finish	1/16"
HL11	100° Flush —— Shear	6Al-4V Titanium	95,000 psi Shear Minimum	.0005 or .0010	750° F or Sub. to Finish	1/16"
HL12	Protruding —— Tension	6Al-4V Titanium	160,000 psi Tensile Minimum	.0005 or .0010	750° F or Sub. to Finish	1/16"
HL13	100° Flush MS24694 Tension	6Al-4V Titanium	160,000 psi Tensile Minimum	.0005 or .0010	750° F or Sub. to Finish	1/16"
HL14	Protruding —— Shear	H-11 Steel Alloy	156,000 psi Shear Minimum	.001	900° F or Sub. to Finish	1/16"
HL15	100° Flush —— Shear	H-11 Steel Alloy	156,000 psi Shear Minimum	.001	900° F or Sub. to Finish	1/16"
HL16	Protruding —— Tension	H-11 Steel Alloy	260,000– 280,000 psi Tensile	.001	900° F or Sub. to Finish	1/16"
HL17	100° Flush MS24694 Tension	H-11 Steel Alloy	260,000– 280,000 psi Tensile	.001	900° F or Sub. to Finish	1/16"
HL18	Protruding —— Shear	Alloy Steel	95,000 psi Shear Minimum	.001	450° F	1/16"
HL19	100° Flush —— Shear	Alloy Steel	95,000 psi Shear Minimum	.001	450° F	1/16"
HL20	Protruding —— Tension	Alloy Steel	160,000– 180,000 psi Tensile	.001	450° F	1/16"
HL21	100° Flush MS24694 Tension	Alloy Steel	160,000– 180,000 psi Tensile	.001	450° F	1/16"

HI-SHEAR CORPORATION (Patent Holder) — Federal Code Ident. No. 73197
VOI-SHAN DIV., VSI CORP. (Licensee) — Federal Code Ident. No. 92215
STANDARD PRESSED STEEL CO. (Licensee) — Federal Code Ident. No. 56878

IDENTIFICATION CHART

Issued: 3-20-68
Revised: October 1972

RECOMMENDED COMPANION HI-LOK COLLARS		NEXT OVERSIZE	CHARACTERISTICS
HL70 HL79 HL82	HL94 HL97 HL379	HL110	Used when weight conservation is essential and where pin shank and hole tolerances are critical. Anti-galling finish available for use with all types of Hi-Lok collar materials.
HL70 HL79 HL82	HL94 HL97 HL379	HL111	Used when weight conservation is essential and where pin shank and hole tolerances are critical. Anti-galling finish available for use with all types of Hi-Lok collar materials.
HL75 HL86	HL198 HL280	HL112	Used when weight conservation is essential and where pin shank and hole tolerances are critical. Anti-galling finish available for use with all types of Hi-Lok collar materials.
HL75 HL86	HL198 HL280	HL113	Used when weight conservation is essential and where pin shank and hole tolerances are critical. Anti-galling finish available for use with all types of Hi-Lok collar materials.
HL288 HL574		HL214	Used in high temperature applications where pin shank and hole close tolerances are required.
HL288 HL574		HL215	Used in high temperature applications where pin shank and hole close tolerances are required.
HL89 HL273		HL216	Used in high temperature applications where pin shank and hole close tolerances are required.
HL89 HL273		HL217	Used in high temperature applications where pin shank and hole close tolerances are required.
HL70 HL79 HL82	HL94 HL97 HL175	HL62	Used where pin shank and hole close tolerances are required.
HL70 HL79 HL82	HL94 HL97 HL175	HL63	Used where pin shank and hole close tolerances are required.
HL75 HL86 HL87		HL64	Used where pin shank and hole close tolerances are required.
HL75 HL86 HL87		HL65	Used where pin shank and hole close tolerances are required.

STANDARDS COMMITTEE
FOR HI-LOK® PRODUCTS
2600 SKYPARK DRIVE, TORRANCE, CALIFORNIA 90509

						HI-LOK PIN
HI-LOK PIN PART NO.	PIN HEAD STYLE APPLICATION	MATERIAL	HEAT TREAT	SHANK DIA. TOL.	SUGGESTED MAXIMUM TEMP. FOR USE	GRIP VARIATION
HL22	Protruding — Shear	7075-T6 Aluminum Alloy	Spec. MIL-H-6088	.001	250°F	1/16"
HL23	100° Flush MS20426 — Shear	7075-T6 Aluminum Alloy	Spec. MIL-H-6088	.001	250°F	1/16"
HL24	100° Flush — Sealing	6Al-4V Titanium	95,000 psi Shear Minimum	.0005	Subject to O-ring Limits	1/16"
HL25	100° Flush — Sealing	431 Stainless Steel	125,000 psi Shear Minimum	.0005	Subject to O-ring Limits	1/16"
HL26	Protruding — Shear	Inconel X-750	95,000 psi Shear Minimum	.0005	1200°F	1/16"
HL27	100° Flush — Shear	Inconel X-750	95,000 psi Shear Minimum	.0005	1200°F	1/16"
HL28	100° Flush — Shear	305 Stainless Steel	Annealed	.001	700°F	1/16"
HL29	100° Flush MS24694 — Tension	7075-T6 Aluminum Alloy	Spec. MIL-H-6088	.001	250°F	1/16"
HL30	Protruding — Shear	431 Stainless Steel	125,000 psi Shear Minimum	.0005 or .0010	400°F	1/16"
HL31	100° Flush — Shear	431 Stainless Steel	125,000 psi Shear Minimum	.0005 or .0010	400°F	1/16"
HL32	Protruding — Tension	431 Stainless Steel	125,000 psi Shear Minimum	.0005 or .0010	400°F	1/16"
HL33	100° Flush MS24694 — Tension	431 Stainless Steel	125,000 psi Shear Minimum	.0005 or .0010	400°F	1/16"

HI-SHEAR CORPORATION (Patent Holder) — Federal Code Ident. No. 73197
VOI-SHAN DIV., VSI CORP. (Licensee) — Federal Code Ident. No. 92215
STANDARD PRESSED STEEL CO. (Licensee) — Federal Code Ident. No. 56878

IDENTIFICATION CHART

RECOMMENDED COMPANION HI-LOK COLLARS	NEXT OVERSIZE	CHARACTERISTICS
HL77 HL182 HL277	HL122	Has higher shear and tension allowables than DD rivets. Interchangeable with MS20470 rivets.
HL77 HL182 HL277	HL123	Has higher shear and tension allowables than DD rivets. Interchangeable with MS20426 rivets.
HL70 HL79 HL82	HL124	Sealing Hi-Lok with silicone or synthetic rubber O-ring. Used when weight conservation is critical and pin shank and hole tolerances are critical.
HL70 HL79 HL86	HL125	Sealing Hi-Lok with general purpose Aromatic Fuel Resistant O-ring. Used in high strength applications where shank and hole tolerances are critical.
HL70 HL88 HL79 HL94 HL82 HL97	——	Used in high temperature shear applications where pin shank and hole close tolerances are required.
HL70 HL88 HL79 HL94 HL82 HL97	——	Used in high temperature shear applications where pin shank and hole close tolerances are required.
HL70 HL79 HL82	——	Stud pin, non-magnetic.
HL77 HL182 HL277	HL129	Has higher tension allowables than HL23.
HL70 HL94 HL79 HL97 HL82 HL175	HL66	Used in high strength applications where shank and hole tolerances are critical.
HL70 HL94 HL79 HL97 HL82 HL175	HL67	Used in high strength applications where shank and hole tolerances are critical
HL73 HL87 HL75 HL89 HL86 HL273	HL36	Used in high strength applications where shank and hole tolerances are critical.
HL73 HL87 HL75 HL89 HL86 HL273	HL37	Used in high strength applications where shank and hole tolerances are critical.

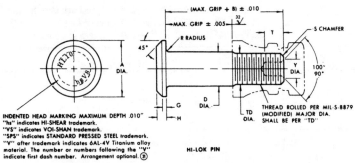

INDENTED HEAD MARKING MAXIMUM DEPTH .010"
"hs" indicates HI-SHEAR trademark.
"VS" indicates VOI-SHAN trademark.
"SPS" indicates STANDARD PRESSED STEEL trademark.
"V" after trademark indicates 6AL-4V Titanium alloy
material. The number or numbers following the "V"
indicate first dash number. Arrangement optional. ®

HI-LOK PIN

FIRST DASH NO.	NOM. DIA.	A DIA.	B REF.	D DIA. 6		TD DIA.	G REF.	H	
				WITHOUT COATING OR SOLID FILM LUBE	WITH COATING OR SOLID FILM LUBE				
✶ ✶ − 5	5/32	.262 .242	.312	.1635 .1630	.1635 .1625	.1595 .1570	.020	.047 .037	
− 6	3/16	.315 .295	.325	.1895 .1890	.1895 .1885	.1840 .1810	.025	.055 .045	
− 8	1/4	.412 .387	.395	.2495 .2490	.2495 .2485	.2440 .2410	.030	.069 .059	
− 10	5/16	.505 .475	.500	.3120 .3115	.3120 .3110	.3060 .3020	.035	.078 .068	
− 12	3/8	.600 .565	.545	.3745 .3740	.3745 .3735	.3680 .3640	.040	.088 .078	
− 14	7/16	.676 .641	.635	.4370 .4365	.4370 .4360	.4310 .4260	.045	.105 .093	
− 16	1/2	.770 .735	.685	.4995 .4990	.4995 .4985	.4930 .4880	.050	.115 .103	
− 18	9/16	.864 .829	.770	.5615 .5610	.5615 .5605	.5550 .5500	.055	.127 .112	
− 20	5/8	.953 .918	.825	.6240 .6235	.6240 .6230	.6180 .6120	.060	.137 .122	
− 24	3/4	1.108 1.066	1.050	.7490 .7485	.7490 .7480	.7430 .7370	.070	.151 .136	
− 28	7/8	1.285 1.241	1.210	.8740 .8735	.8740 .8730	.8680 .8610	.090	.187 .172	
− 32	1	1.468 1.424	1.390	.9990 .9985	.9990 .9980	.9930 .9860	.110	.218 .203	

✶ ✶ -5 SIZE MUST BE INSTALLED USING A TORQUE CONTROLLED HEX KEY.

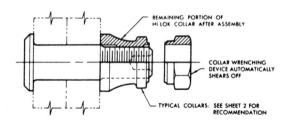

HI-LOK PIN AND COLLAR AFTER ASSEMBLY

R RAD.	S CHAMFER REF.	THREAD	SOCKET			DOUBLE SHEAR POUNDS MINIMUM	TENSION POUNDS MINIMUM
			W HEX.	T DEPTH	Y DIA.		
.025 .015	1/32" x 37°	8-32UNJC-3A Modified	.0645 .0635	.135 .115	.090 .075	4,010	1,940
.025 .015	1/32" x 37°	10-32UNJF-3A Modified	.0806 .0791	.135 .115	.119 .104	5,380	2,500
.025 .015	1/32" x 37°	1/4-28UNJF-3A Modified	.0967 .0947	.150 .130	.142 .122	9,300	4,300
.030 .020	3/64" x 37°	5/16-24UNJF-3A Modified	.1295 .1270	.170 .150	.180 .160	14,600	6,300
.030 .020	3/64" x 37°	3/8-24UNJF-3A Modified	.1617 .1582	.200 .180	.217 .197	21,000	8,700
.030 .020	3/64" x 37°	7/16-20UNJF-3A Modified	.1930 .1895	.230 .210	.253 .233	28,600	12,100
.030 .020	3/64" x 37°	1/2-20UNJF-3A Modified	.2242 .2207	.260 .240	.289 .269	37,300	15,300
.040 .025	1/16" x 37°	9/16-18UNJF-3A Modified	.2555 .2520	.290 .270	.326 .306	47,200	19,000
.040 .025	1/16" x 37°	5/8-18UNJF-3A Modified	.2555 .2520	.330 .305	.326 .306	58,300	23,000
.045 .030	1/16" x 37°	3/4-16UNJF-3A Modified	.3185 .3150	.395 .365	.398 .378	83,900	30,700
.050 .035	5/64" x 37°	7/8-14UNJF-3A Modified	.3820 .3780	.455 .425	.471 .451	114,000	45,000
.060 .045	5/64" x 37°	1-12UNJF-3A Modified	.5100 .5040	.580 .550	.618 .598	149,000	60,900

SEE COLLAR STANDARDS FOR
COLLAR STRENGTHS. LOWER STRENGTH
(PIN OR COLLAR) DETERMINES
SYSTEM STRENGTH.

U.S. patents 2,882,773; 2,927,491; 2,940,495; 3,027,789; 3,138,987; design patent 191,883; other U.S. and Foreign patents granted and pending; property of Hi-Shear Corporation. "Hi-Lok" and "HL" are Registered Trademarks of Hi-Shear Corporation.

DRAWN	DATE	
Brlej	11-26-62	**hi-Lok' PIN**
APPROVED	**DATE**	PROTRUDING SHEAR HEAD
Cessna	11-26-62	TITANIUM 1/16" GRIP VARIATION
REVISION	**DATE**	**DRAWING NUMBER**
㉛	D. P. S. 3-22-76	**HL10** SHEET 1 OF 2

GENERAL NOTES:

1. Concentricity: "A" to "D" diameter within .010 FIR.
2. Dimensions to be met after finish.
3. Surface texture per ANSI-46.1.
4. Hole preparation per NAS618.
5. Use HL110 for oversize replacement.
6. Maximum "D" diameter may be increased by .0002 to allow for solid film or aluminum coating application.
7. Dimensions to be met before finish for "VY" code only.

CODE:

First dash number indicates nominal diameter in 1/32nds.
Second dash number indicates maximum grip in 1/16ths.
See "Finish" note for explanation of code letters.

MATERIAL: 6Al-4V titanium alloy per Spec. AMS4928 or AMS4967.

HEAT TREAT: 95,000 psi shear minimum.

To prevent setting and galling, the following combinations are recommended.

FINISH:

Code	Description	RECOMMENDED COLLARS
HL10V-( )-( )	= Cetyl alcohol lube per Hi-Shear Spec. 305.	HL70, HL79, HL82, HL84K, HL94V, HL97K, HL97V, HL379V, HL379SY
HL10VAP-( )-( )	= Hi-Kote I aluminum coating per Hi-Shear Spec. 294 and cetyl alcohol lube per Hi-Shear Spec. 305.	HL70, HL79, HL82, HL94, HL97
HL10VAZ-( )-( )	= Hi-Kote I aluminum coating per Hi-Shear Spec. 294 with color code black on thread end, and cetyl alcohol lube per Hi-Shear Spec. 305.	HL70, HL79, HL82, HL94, HL97
HL10VF-( )-( )	= Surface coating per Hi-Shear Spec. 306, Type I, color blue, and cetyl alcohol lube per Hi-Shear Spec. 305.	HL70, HL79, HL82, HL94K, HL94V, HL97K, HL97V, HL379V, HL379SY
HL10VLJ-( )-( )	= Surface coating per Hi-Shear Spec. 306, Type II, and solid film lube per MIL-L-8937.	HL70, HL79, HL82, HL94, HL97
HL10VLV-( )-( )	= Phosphate fluoride treat and Exna-Lube No. 382 (Everlube Corp.).	HL70, HL79, HL82, HL379, HL379V, HL379SY
HL10VR-( )-( )	= Surface coating per Hi-Shear Spec. 306, Type II, and solid film lube per "Electrofilm" 4396.	HL70, HL79, HL82, HL94, HL97
HL10VRA-( )-( )	= Phosphate fluoride treat with color code red on thread end and cetyl alcohol lube per Hi-Shear Spec. 305.	HL70, HL79, HL82, HL84K, HL94V, HL97K, HL97V, HL379V, HL379SY
HL10VSY-( )-( )	= Phosphate fluoride treat, solid film lube per MIL-L-8937 and color code red on thread end.	HL70, HL79, HL82, HL84, HL97, HL379, HL379V, HL379SY
HL10VT-( )-( )	= Surface coating per Hi-Shear Spec. 306, Type I, color pink, and cetyl alcohol lube per Hi-Shear Spec. 305.	HL70, HL79, HL82, HL94K, HL94V, HL97K, HL97V, HL379V, HL379SY

HL10VTA-( )-( ) = Anodize Ti-Shield III and Hi-Kote II solid film lube per Hi-Shear Spec. 292 plus cetyl alcohol lube per Hi-Shear Spec. 305. _____ HL70, HL79, HL82, HL84, HL97

HL10VTB-( )-( ) = Hi-Kote II solid film lube per Hi-Shear Spec. 292 and cetyl alcohol lube per Hi-Shear Spec. 305. _____ HL70, HL79, HL82, HL84, HL97

HL10VTF-( )-( ) = Hi-Kote II solid film lube per Hi-Shear Spec. 292. _____ HL70TF, HL84TF

HL10VTL-( )-( ) = Anodize per Hi-Shear Ti-Shield III, solid film lube per DAG-258, and cetyl alcohol lube per Hi-Shear Spec. 305. or anodize per Tiodize Type II. solid film lube per TI-O-LUBE TAL-58, and cetyl alcohol lube per Hi-Shear Spec. 305. _____ HL70, HL79, HL82, HL84, HL97

HL10VTT-( )-( ) = Translube. _____ HL70TT

HL10VUE-( )-( ) = Surface coating per Hi-Shear Spec. 306, Type II, and cetyl alcohol lube per Hi-Shear Spec. 305. _____ HL70, HL79, HL82, HL84, HL84K, HL84V, HL97, HL97K, HL97V, HL379, HL379V, HL379SY

HL10VV-( )-( ) = Solid film lube per "Labeco" 2123, Type II. _____ HL70, HL79, HL82, HL84, HL84K, HL84V, HL97, HL97K, HL97V

[7] HL10VY-( )-( ) = Surface coating per Hi-Shear Spec. 306, Type I, color blue, and solid film lubricant per M88 (British Aircraft Corp. Spec. MP-1011). _____ HL70, HL79, HL82, HL84, HL97, HL379

SPECIFICATION: Hi-Lok Product Specification 342.

HOW TO ORDER EXAMPLES:

Pin Part Number Only

HL10VUE-8-8
 │   │ └── 8/16 or 1/2 Maximum Grip Length
 │   └── Type II, Black Finish
 └── Pin Part Number

8/32 or 1/4 Nominal Diameter Pin

Pin and Collar Assembly Part Number Combination

HL10VUE70-8-8
 │   │ └── Size and Grip Length, See Above Example
 │   └── Collar Part Number
 │   └── Pin Finish
 └── Pin Part Number

┌─────────────────┐
│   │
│   HL10   │
│   SHEET 2 OF 2 │
│   │
└─────────────────┘

hi-Lok® hi-tigue® PRODUCTS

2600 SKYPARK DRIVE, TORRANCE, CALIFORNIA 90509

						HI-LOK® HI-TIGUE®
HI-LOK HI-TIGUE PIN PART NO.	PIN HEAD STYLE APPLICATION	MATERIAL	HEAT TREAT	SHANK DIA. TOL.	SUGGESTED MAXIMUM TEMP. FOR USE	GRIP VARIATION
HLT10	Protruding — Shear	6Al-4V Titanium Alloy	95,000 psi Shear Minimum	.001	600°	1/16"
HLT11	100° Flush Crown Shear	6Al-4V Titanium Alloy	95,000 psi Shear Minimum	.001	600°	1/16"
HLT12	Protruding — Tension	6Al-4V Titanium Alloy	160,000 psi Tensile Minimum	.001	600°	1/16"
HLT13	100° Flush MS24694 Tension	6Al-4V Titanium Alloy	160,000 psi Tensile Minimum	.001	600°	1/16"
HLT18	Protruding — Shear	Alloy Steel	95,000 psi Shear Minimum	.001	450°	1/16"
HLT19	100° Flush Crown Shear	Alloy Steel	95,000 psi Shear Minimum	.001	450°	1/16"
HLT22	Protruding — Shear	6Al-6V-2Sn Titanium Alloy	108,000 psi Shear Minimum	.001	600°	1/16"
HLT23	100° Flush Crown Shear	6Al-6V-2Sn Titanium Alloy	108,000 psi Shear Minimum	.001	600°	1/16"
HLT24	Protruding — Tension	6Al-6V-2Sn Titanium Alloy	180,000- 200,000 psi Tensile	.001	600°	1/16"
HLT25	100° Flush MS24694 Tension	6Al-6V-2Sn Titanium Alloy	180,000- 200,000 psi Tensile	.001	600°	1/16"
HLT314	Protruding — Shear	H-11 Steel Alloy	132,000 psi Shear Minimum	.0010	900°	1/16"
HLT315	100° Flush — Shear	H-11 Steel Alloy	132,000 psi Shear Minimum	.0010	900°	1/16"

PIN IDENTIFICATION CHART

RECOMMENDED COMPANION HI-LOK HI-TIGUE COLLARS	NEXT OVERSIZE	CHARACTERISTICS
HLT70 HLT94 HLT71 HLT97	HLT110	Used where weight conservation and high fatigue life is critical. Pins are designed for easy installation in interference fit holes. Anti-galling finish available for use with all types of Hi-Lok Hi-Tigue collar materials.
HLT70 HLT94 HLT71 HLT97	HLT111	Used where weight conservation and high fatigue life is critical. Pins are designed for easy installation in interference fit holes. Anti-galling finish available for use with all types of Hi-Lok Hi-Tigue collar materials.
HLT78 HLT87	HLT112	Used where weight conservation and high fatigue life is critical. Pins are designed for easy installation in interference fit holes. Anti-galling finish available for use with all types of Hi-Lok Hi-Tigue collar materials.
HLT78 HLT87	HLT113	Used where weight conservation and high fatigue life is critical. Pins are designed for each installation in interference fit holes. Anti-galling finish available for use with all types of Hi-Lok Hi-Tigue collar materials.
HLT70 HLT94 HLT71 HLT97	HLT118	Pins are designed for easy installation in interference fit holes.
HLT70 HLT94 HLT71 HLT97	HLT119	Pins are designed for easy installation in interference fit holes.
HLT70 HLT94 HLT71 HLT97	HLT122	Same as HLT10 except for material and heat treat.
HLT70 HLT94 HLT71 HLT97	HLT123	Same as HLT11 except for material and heat treat.
HLT78 HLT87	HLT124	Same as HLT12 except for material and heat treat.
HLT78 HLT87	HLT125	Same as HLT13 except for material and heat treat.
HLT73	HLT414	Used where very high shear and high fatigue life is critical. Pins are designed for easy installation in interference fit holes.
HLT73	HLT415	Used where very high shear and high fatigue life is critical. Pins are designed for easy installation in interference fit holes.

hi-Lok® hi-tigue® PRODUCTS
2600 SKYPARK DRIVE, TORRANCE, CALIFORNIA 90509

HI-LOK® HI-TIGUE® PIN

HI-LOK HI-TIGUE PIN PART NO.	PIN HEAD STYLE APPLICATION	MATERIAL	HEAT TREAT	SHANK DIA. TOL.	SUGGESTED MAXIMUM TEMP. FOR USE	GRIP VARIATION	
HLT318	Protruding — Shear	Alloy Steel	95,000 psi Shear Minimum	.0010	450°	1/16"	
HLT319	100° Flush — Shear	Alloy Steel	95,000 psi Shear Minimum	.0010	450°	1/16"	
HLT410	Protruding — Shear	6Al-4V Titanium Alloy	95,000 psi Shear Minimum	.0005	600°	1/16"	
HLT411	100° Flush — Shear	6Al-4V Titanium Alloy	95,000 psi Shear Minimum	.0005	600°	1/16"	
HLT412	Protruding — Tension	6Al-4V Titanium Alloy	160,000 psi Tensile Minimum	.0005	600°	1/16"	
HLT413	100° Flush — Tension	6Al-4V Titanium Alloy	160,000 psi Tensile Minimum	.0005	600°	1/16"	
HLT510	Protruding — Shear	6Al-4V Titanium Alloy	95,000 psi Shear Minimum	.001	450°	1/16"	
HLT511	100° Flush Crown Shear	6Al-4V Titanium Alloy	95,000 psi Shear Minimum	.001	450°	1/16"	
HLT512	Protruding — Tension	6Al-4V Titanium Alloy	160,000 psi Shear Minimum	.001	450°	1/16"	
HLT513	100° Flush MS24694 Tension	6Al-4V Titanium Alloy	160,000 psi Tensile Minimum	.001	450°	1/16"	
HLT803	70° Flush Crown Shear	6Al-4V Titanium Alloy	95,000 psi Shear Minimum	.0010	600°	1/16"	

STANDARDS MANUAL

IDENTIFICATION CHART

RECOMMENDED COMPANION HI-LOK HI-TIGUE COLLARS	NEXT OVERSIZE	CHARACTERISTICS
HLT70 HLT94 HLT71 HLT97	——	Used where high fatigue life is critical. Pins are designed for easy installation in interference fit holes.
HLT70 HLT94 HLT71 HLT97	——	Used where high fatigue life is critical. Pins are designed for easy installation in interference fit holes.
HLT70 HLT94 HLT71 HLT97	HLT110	Same as HLT10 except diameter tolerance.
HLT70 HLT94 HLT71 HLT97	HLT109	Same as HLT11 except diameter tolerance.
HLT78 HLT86	HLT112	Same as HLT12 except diameter tolerance.
HLT78 HLT86	HLT113	Same as HLT13 except diameter tolerance.
HLT70 HLT94 HLT71 HLT97	——	Same as HLT10 except finish with cadmium plate.
HLT70 HLT94 HLT71 HLT97	——	Same as HLT11 except finish with cadmium plate.
HLT78 HLT87	——	Same as HLT13 except finish with cadmium plate.
HLT78 HLT87	——	Same as HLT13 except finish with cadmium plate.
HLT1070	HLT807	Used where weight conservation and high fatigue life is critical. Designed for easy installation in interference fit holes with 82° countersinks for head interference also.

STANDARDS COMMITTEE FOR
HI-LOK® HI-TIGUE® PRODUCTS
2800 SKYPARK DRIVE, TORRANCE, CALIFORNIA 90500

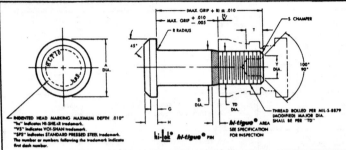

— INDENTED HEAD MARKING MAXIMUM DEPTH .010"
"hs" indicates HI-SHEAR trademark.
"VS" indicates VOI-SHAN trademark.
"SPS" indicates STANDARD PRESSED STEEL trademark.
The number or numbers following the trademark indicate first dash number.

hi-lok® hi-tigue® PIN

FIRST DASH NO.	NOM. DIA.	A DIA.	B REF.	D DIA. WITHOUT SOLID FILM LUBE	D DIA. WITH SOLID FILM LUBE	TD DIA.	G REF.	H	R RAD.
–5	5/32	.262 .242	.312	.1695 .1690	.1695 .1685	.1595 .1570	.020	.047 .037	.025 .015
–6	3/16	.315 .295	.325	.1955 .1950	.1965 .1945	.1840 .1810	.025	.055 .045	.025 .015
–8	1/4	.412 .387	.395	.2555 .2550	.2555 .2545	.2440 .2410	.030	.069 .059	.025 .015
–10	5/16	.505 .475	.500	.3180 .3175	.3180 .3170	.3060 .3020	.035	.078 .068	.030 .020
–12	3/8	.600 .565	.545	.3805 .3800	.3805 .3795	.3680 .3640	.040	.088 .078	.030 .020
–14	7/16	.676 .641	.635	.4430 .4425	.4430 .4420	.4310 .4260	.045	.105 .093	.030 .020
–16	1/2	.770 .735	.685	.5065 .5050	.5065 .5045	.4930 .4880	.060	.115 .103	.030 .020

Ⓓ GENERAL NOTES:
1. Concentricity: "A" to "D" diameter within .010 FIR.
2. Dimensions to be met after finish.
3. Surface texture per ANSI B46.1.
4. Hole preparation per NAS618 (Column "B") for interference application.
5. Use HLT110 for oversize replacement.
6. Install per Hi-Shear Spec. 299.
7. Minimum required for head and Hi-Tigue feature.

MATERIAL: 6Al-4V titanium alloy per Spec. AMS4928 or AMS4967.

HEAT TREAT: 95,000 psi shear minimum.

FINISH: HLT10-( )-( )   = Cetyl alcohol lube per Hi-Shear Spec. 305.
HLT10AP-( )-( ) = Hi-Kote 1 per Hi-Shear Spec. 294, and cetyl alcohol lube per Hi-Shear Spec. 305.
HLT10TB-( )-( ) = Hi-Kote 2 and cetyl alcohol lube per Hi-Shear Spec. 305.

SPECIFICATION: Hi-Lok Hi-Tigue Product Specification 342.

① HI-SHEAR CORPORATION, U.S.A.   (Patent Holder) U.S. Federal Code I.D. No. 73197
        Division of Hi-Shear Industries Inc.
VSI-SHAN, Division of VSI Corp., U.S.A.   (Licensee) U.S. Federal Code I.D. No. 92215
SPS TECHNOLOGIES, U.S.A.   (Licensee) U.S. Federal Code I.D. No. 06079
LITTON FASTENING SYSTEMS, U.S.A.
        Division of Litton Systems, Inc.   (Licensee) U.S. Federal Code I.D. No. 97929

KAMAX-WERKE, Germany   (Licensee)
        Rudolph Kellerman GmbH & Co.
ST. CHAMOND-GRANAT, S.A. France   (Licensee)
TOKYO SCREW COMPANY, Japan   (Licensee)

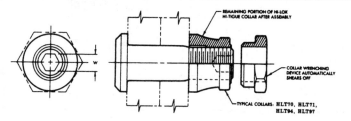

REMAINING PORTION OF HI-LOK HI-TIGUE COLLAR AFTER ASSEMBLY

COLLAR WRENCHING DEVICE AUTOMATICALLY SHEARS OFF

TYPICAL COLLARS: HLT70, HLT71, HLT94, HLT97

hi-Lok® hi-tigue® PIN and COLLAR AFTER ASSEMBLY

SEE COLLAR STANDARDS FOR COLLAR STRENGTHS. LOWER STRENGTH (PIN OR COLLAR) DETERMINES SYSTEM STRENGTH.

S CHAMFER REF.	THREAD	SOCKET			DOUBLE SHEAR POUNDS MINIMUM	TENSION POUNDS MINIMUM	⑦ MIN. GRIP LENGTH
		W HEX.	T DEPTH	Y DIA.			
1/32" x 37°	8-32UNJC-3A	.0645	.100	.090	4,210	1,940	-2
	Modified	.0635 ①	.080	.075			
1/32" x 37°	10-32UNJF-3A	.0806	.100	.119	5,550	2,500	-2
	Modified	.0791	.080	.104			
1/32" x 37°	1/4-28UNJF-3A	.0967	.110	.142	9,620	4,300	-2
	Modified	.0947	.090	.122			
3/64" x 37°	5/16-24UNJF-3A	.1295	.130	.180	14,890	6,300	-2
	Modified	.1270	.110	.160			
3/64" x 37°	3/8-24UNJF-3A	.1617	.160	.217	21,430	8,700	-3
	Modified	.1562	.140	.197			
3/64" x 37°	7/16-20UNJF-3A	.1930	.190	.253	29,000	12,100	-4
	Modified	.1895	.170	.233			
3/64" x 37°	1/2-20UNJF-3A	.2242	.220	.289	37,900	15,300	-4
	Modified	.2207	.200	.269			

CODE: First dash number indicates nominal diameter in 32nds.
Second dash number indicates maximum grip in 16ths.
See "Finish" note for explanation of code letters.

HOW TO ORDER EXAMPLES:

Pin Part Number Only
HLT10-8-8
　　　└── 8/16 or 1/2 Maximum Grip Length
　　└── 8/32 or 1/4 Nominal Diameter Pin
　└── Pin Part Number

Pin and Collar Assembly Part Number Combination
HLT1070-8-8
　　　└── Size and Grip Length, See Above Example
　　└── Collar Part Number
　└── Pin Part Number

U.S. patents 3,136,987; 3,390,906; 3,578,367; and foreign patents. "Hi-Lok," "HL," "Hi-Tigue," and "HLT" are Registered Trademarks of Hi-Shear Corporation.

DRAWN	DATE	
VAN	6-25-68	**hi-Lok® hi-tigue® PIN**
APPROVED	DATE	PROTRUDING SHEAR HEAD TITANIUM 1/16" GRIP VARIATION
R. TIAN	7-25-68	
REVISION	DATE	DRAWING NUMBER
①	D. P. S. 10-29-81	**HLT10**

STANDARDS COMMITTEE
FOR HI-LOK® PRODUCTS
2600 SKYPARK DRIVE, TORRANCE, CALIFORNIA 90509

						HI-LOK COLLAR
HI-LOK COLLAR PART NO.	COLLAR MATERIAL	COLLAR FINISH COLOR OR PLATING	WASHER MATERIAL	WASHER FINISH COLOR OR PLATING	SUGGESTED MAXIMUM TEMP. FOR USE	GRIP VARIATION
HL70	2024-T6 Aluminum Alloy	See Drawing	2024 or 5052 Aluminum Alloy	Blue or Grey	300°F	1/16"
HL75	303 Series Stainless Steel	See Drawing	17-4PH, 17-7PH or PH15-7Mo Stainless Steel	See Drawing	700°F or Sub. to Finish	1/16"
HL77	2024-T6 Aluminum Alloy	See Drawing	2024 or 5052 Aluminum Alloy	Black	300°F	1/16"
HL78	A-286 Hi-Temp. Alloy	See Drawing	300 Series Stainless Steel	See Drawing	1200°F or Sub. to Finish	1/16"
HL79	2024-T6 Aluminum Alloy	Red	N/A	N/A	300°F	1/16"
HL82	2024-T6 Aluminum Alloy	See Drawing	17-4PH, 17-7PH or PH15-7Mo Stainless Steel	See Drawing	300°F	1/16"
HL87	303 Series Stainless Steel	See Drawing	300 Series Stainless Steel	Cadmium Plate	700°F or Sub. to Finish	1/16"
HL89	17-4PH Stainless Steel	See Drawing	17-4PH, 17-7PH or PH15-7Mo Stainless Steel	See Drawing	700°F or Sub. to Finish	1/16"
HL182	2024-T6 Aluminum Alloy	See Drawing	17-4PH, 17-7PH or PH15-7Mo Stainless Steel	See Drawing	300°F	1/16"
HL198	6Al-4V Titanium Alloy	See Drawing	300 Series Stainless Steel	See Drawing	750°F or Sub. to Finish	1/16"
HL199	6Al-4V Titanium Alloy	See Drawing	300 Series Stainless Steel	See Drawing	750°F or Sub. to Finish	1/16"
HL273	17-4PH Stainless Steel	See Drawing	N/A	N/A	700°F or Sub. to Finish	1/16"
HL379	6Al-4V Titanium Alloy	See Drawing	300 Series Stainless Steel	See Drawing	750°F or Sub. to Finish	1/16"

HI-SHEAR CORPORATION (Patent Holder) — Federal Code Ident. No. 73197
VOI-SHAN DIV., VSI CORP. (Licensee) — Federal Code Ident. No. 92215
STANDARD PRESSED STEEL CO. (Licensee) — Federal Code Ident. No. 56878

IDENTIFICATION CHART   Issue Date: November 1972

APPLICATION	NEXT OVERSIZE	CHARACTERISTICS
Shear	HL79 or HL80	For use with shear head pins except those made of aluminum alloy. Optional washer.
Tension	HL375	Self-aligning collar assembly. For use on sloped surfaces up to 7° maximum. Fits standard and 1/64" oversize tension head pins.
Shear	HL377	For use with aluminum alloy pins in shear applications. Optional washer.
Tension	HL278	Used in high temperature applications. Anti-galling lubricant available for use in titanium pins. Optional washer.
Shear	HL84	For standard and 1/64" oversize for HL70. For use with Hi-Lok Automatic Feed Driver Tools and shear head pins except those made of aluminum alloy.
Shear	HL382	Self-aligning collar assembly. For use on sloped surfaces up to 7° maximum. Fits standard and 1/64" oversize pins. Use with shear head pins except those made of aluminum alloy.
Tension	HL93	For standard and 1/64" oversize for HL86. Optional washer.
Tension	HL289	Self-aligning collar assembly. For use on sloped surfaces up to 7° maximum. Fits standard and 1/64" oversize tension head pins.
Shear	—	Self-aligning collar assembly. For use on sloped surfaces up to 7° maximum. Fits standard and 1/64" oversize aluminum alloy pins.
Tension	—	For use on standard and 1/64" oversize tension head pins. Optional washer.
Special	—	Special application.
Tension	HL373	For standard and 1/64" oversize for HL73.
Shear	—	For use on standard and 1/64" oversize shear head pins.

STANDARDS COMMITTEE
FOR HI-LOK® PRODUCTS
2600 SKYPARK DRIVE, TORRANCE, CALIFORNIA 90509

HI-SHEAR CORPORATION (Patent Holder) — Federal Code Ident. No. 73197
VOI-SHAN DIV., VSI CORP. (License) — Federal Code Ident. No. 92215
STANDARD PRESSED STEEL CO. (License) — Federal Code Ident. No. 56878

STANDARDS
MANUAL

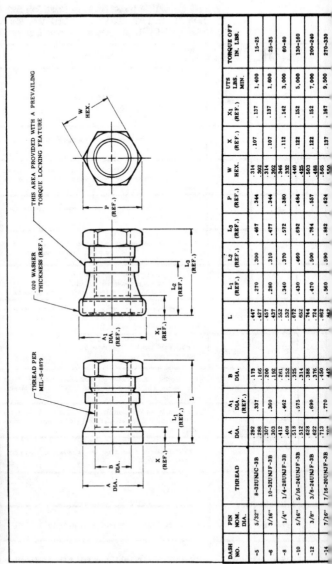

THREAD PER MIL-S-8879

.020 WASHER THICKNESS (REF.)

THIS AREA PROVIDED WITH A PREVAILING TORQUE LOCKING FEATURE

DASH NO.	PIN NOM. DIA.	THREAD	A DIA.	A₁ DIA. (REF.)	B DIA.	L	L₁ (REF.)	L₂ (REF.)	L₃ (REF.)	P (REF.)	W HEX.	X (REF.)	X₁ (REF.)	UTS LBS. MIN.	TORQUE OFF IN. LBS.
-5	5/32"	8-32UNJC-3B	.292 .288	.337	.173 .166	.447 .427	.270	.300	.667	.344	.314 .302	.107	.137	1,400	15-25
-6	3/16"	10-32UNJF-3B	.307 .303	.360	.200 .192	.457 .437	.280	.310	.477	.344	.314 .302	.107	.137	1,600	25-35
-8	1/4"	1/4-28UNJF-3B	.412 .408	.462	.261 .252	.552 .532	.340	.370	.572	.380	.346 .332	.112	.142	3,000	60-80
-10	5/16"	5/16-24UNJF-3B	.518 .512	.575	.325 .314	.672 .652	.430	.460	.692	.484	.440 .425	.122	.152	5,000	130-160
-12	3/8"	3/8-24UNJF-3B	.628 .622	.690	.388 .376	.744 .724	.470	.500	.764	.557	.503 .488	.122	.152	7,000	200-240
-14	7/16"	7/16-20UNJF-3B	.713 .703	.770	.450 .442	.862 .842	.560	.590	.882	.624	.565 .550	.137	.167	9,500	270-330

-18	9/16"	9/16-18UNJF-3B	NOTE: Use HL79-18
-20	5/8"	5/8-1NUNJF-3B	NOTE: Use HL79-20
-24	3/4"	3/4-16UNJF-3B	NOTE: Use HL79-24
-28	7/8"	7/8-14UNJF-3B	NOTE: Use HL79-28
-32	1"	1-12UNJF-3B	NOTE: Use HL79-32

NOTES:
1. Go thread gage penetration shall be 3/4 of one revolution minimum.
2. Dimensions apply after finish.
3. Use HL79 for oversize replacement.

MATERIAL: Collar — 2024 aluminum alloy per QQ-A-430 or QQ-A-225/6.
Washer — "TW" = 5052 aluminum alloy per QQ-A-250/8, or 2024 aluminum alloy per QQ-A-250/4 or QQ-A-250/5.

HEAT TREAT: Collar — Age to T6 condition per MIL-H-6088.
Washer — "TW" = Age to T6 condition per MIL-H-6088 (for 2024 only).

FINISH: Collar — HL70-( ) = Anodize per Spec. MIL-A-8625, dye color red, and cetyl alcohol lube per Hi-Shear Spec. 305.
HL70D-( ) = Anodize per Spec. MIL-A-8625 and solid film lube per MIL-L-8937.
HL70K-( ) = Anodize per Spec. MIL-A-8625 and solid film lube per "Lubeco" 905.
HL70LZ-( ) = Anodize per Spec. MIL-A-8625, dye color red, and lauric acid lube per Hi-Shear Spec. 305.
HL70TF-( ) = Anodize per MIL-A-8625 and Hi-Kote 2 solid film lube per Hi-Shear Spec. 292.
HL70TT-( ) = Anodize per Spec. MIL-A-8625, dye color red, and translube.
Collar and Washer — HL70TW-( ) = Collar finish is the same as HL70-( ). Washer finish is anodize per Spec. MIL-A-8625, dye color grey, or blue (for 2024 only).
HL70DTW-( ) = Collar finish is the same as HL70D-( ). Washer finish is anodize per MIL-A-8625, dye color grey, or blue (for 2024 only).

SPECIFICATION: Hi-Lok Product Specification 345.
CODE: Dash number indicates nominal thread size in 1/32nds.
See "Finish" note for explanation of code letters.
EXAMPLE: HL70-8 = 1/4-28 Hi-Lok collar only.
HL70TW-8 = 1/4-28 Hi-Lok collar with aluminum washer.

VOI-SHAN
1 raised bead indicates
VOI-SHAN identification.

STANDARD PRESSED STEEL
2 raised beads indicate STANDARD
PRESSED STEEL identification.

hi-lok® COLLAR

TITLE
2024-T6 ALUMINUM ALLOY
1/16" GRIP VARIATION — SHEAR APPLICATION

DRAWING NUMBER
HL70

U.S. patents 2,883,773; 2,927,491; 2,940,495; 3,027,789; 3,138,987, design patent 191,883; other U.S. and foreign patents granted and pending; property of Hi-Shear Corporation. "Hi-Lok" and "HL" are Registered Trademarks of Hi-Shear Corporation.

	DATE	BY	
DRAWN	7/27/60	VAN	
APPROVED	7-27-60	MEC	
REVISION	3-22-76	D. P. S.	

Appendix

Aircraft Thread and Tap Drill Sizes

The screw and nut combination is probably the most used of machine elements. Certain thread series have, through their extensive use, come to be known as "standard."

CLASSIFICATION OF THREADS

Aircraft bolts, screws, and nuts are threaded in either the NC (American National Coarse) thread series, the NF (American National Fine) thread series, the UNC (American Standard Unified Coarse) thread series, or the UNF (American Standard Unified Fine) thread series. Although they are interchangeable, there is one difference between the American National series and the American Standard Unified series that should be pointed out. In the 1-inch diameter size, the NF thread specified 14 threads per inch (1-14NF), while the UNF thread specifies 12 threads per inch (1-12UNF). Both type threads are designated by the number of times the incline (threads) rotates around a 1-inch length of a given diameter bolt or screw. For example a 4-28 thread indicates that a 1/4-inch diameter bolt has 28 threads in 1 inch of its threaded length (Fig. A-1).

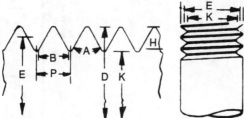

Fig. A-1. A, *thread angle;* B, *base;* D, *major diameter;* E, *pitch diameter;* H, *depth;* K, *minor diameter;* P, *pitch.*

Threads are also designated by class of fit. The class of a thread indicates the tolerance allowed in manufacturing. Class 1 is a loose fit, Class 2 is a free fit, Class 3 is a medium fit, and Class 4 is a close fit.

Aircraft bolts are almost always manufactured in the Class 3, medium fit.

A Class 4 fit requires a wrench to turn the nut onto a bolt whereas a Class 1 fit can easily be turned with the fingers. Generally, aircraft screws are manufactured with a Class 2 thread fit for ease of assembly. The general purpose aircraft bolt, AN3 through AN20, has UNF-3 threads (American Standard Unified Fine, Class 3, medium fit).

Bolts and nuts are also produced with right-handed and left-handed threads; a right-handed thread tightens when turned clockwise; a left-handed thread tightens when turned counterclockwise. Except in special cases, all aircraft bolts have right-handed threads.

TAP DRILL SIZES

National Coarse Thread Series Medium Fit, Class 3 (NC)

Size and threads	Dia. of body	Body drill	Preferred dia. of hole	Tap drill
1–64	.073	47	.0575	No. 53
2–56	.086	42	.0682	No. 51
3–48	.099	37	.078	5⁄64 in.
4–40	.112	31	.0866	No. 44
5–40	.125	29	.0995	No. 39
6–32	.138	27	.1063	No. 36
8–32	.164	18	.1324	No. 29
10–24	.190	10	.1476	No. 26
12–24	.216	2	.1732	No. 17
¼–20	.250	¼	.1990	No. 8
5⁄16–18	.3125	5⁄16	.2559	F
3⁄8–16	.375	3⁄8	.3110	5⁄16 in.
7⁄16–14	.4375	7⁄16	.3642	U
½–13	.500	½	.4219	27⁄64 in.
9⁄16–12	.5625	9⁄16	.4776	31⁄64
5⁄8–11	.625	5⁄8	.5315	17⁄32 in.
¾–10	.750	¾	.6480	41⁄64 in.
7⁄8–9	.875	7⁄8	.7307	49⁄64 in.
1–8	1.000	1	.8376	7⁄8 in.

National Fine Thread Series Medium Fit, Class 3 (NF)

Size and threads	Dia. of body	Body drill	Preferred dia. of hole	Tap drill
0–80	.060	52	.0472	3⁄64 in.
1–72	.073	47	.0591	No. 53
2–64	.086	42	.0700	No. 50
3–56	.099	37	.0810	No. 46
4–48	.112	31	.0911	No. 42
5–44	.125	29	.1024	No. 38
6–40	.138	27	.113	No. 33
8–36	.164	18	.136	No. 29
10–32	.190	10	.159	No. 21
12–28	.216	2	.180	No. 15
¼–28	.250	F	.213	No. 3
5⁄16–24	.3125	5⁄16	.2703	I
3⁄8–24	.375	3⁄8	.332	Q
7⁄16–20	.4375	7⁄16	.386	W
½–20	.500	½	.449	7⁄16 in.
9⁄16–18	.5625	9⁄16	.506	½ in.
5⁄8–18	.625	5⁄8	.568	9⁄16 in.
¾–16	.750	¾	.6688	11⁄16 in.
7⁄8–14	.875	7⁄8	.7822	51⁄64 in.
1–14	1.000	1	.9072	59⁄64 in.

National Taper Pipe Thread

Size pipe thread, in.	No. of threads per inch	Outside dia. of pipe for threading		Size pipe reamer, in.	Size tap drill, in.
		Decimal inch	Nearest fraction of inch		
1⁄8	27	.405	13⁄32	1⁄8	21⁄64
¼	18	.540	35⁄64	¼	7⁄16
3⁄8	18	.675	43⁄64	3⁄8	9⁄16
½	14	.840	27⁄32	½	45⁄64
¾	14	1.050	13⁄64	¾	29⁄32

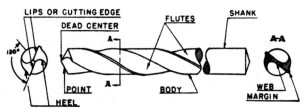

TWIST DRILL SIZES

Decimal equivalent	Fraction	Number or letter	Decimal equivalent	Fraction	Number or letter	Decimal equivalent	Fraction	Number or letter
.0135	...	80	.096*	....	41	.2187	7/32	
.0145	...	79	.098	....	40	.221	....	2
.0156	...	78	.0995	....	39	.228	....	1
.016	1/64		.1015	....	38	.234	....	A
.018	...	77	.104	....	37	.2343	15/64	
.020	...	76	.1065	....	36	.238	....	B
.021	...	75	.1093	7/64		.242	....	C
.0225	...	74	.110	....	35	.246	....	D
.024	...	73	.111	....	34	.250	1/4	E
.025	...	72	.113	....	33	.257	....	F
.026	...	71	.116	....	32	.261	....	G
.028	...	70	.120	....	31	.2656	17/64	
.029	...	69	.125	1/8		.266	....	H
.031	...	68	.1285	....	30	.272	....	I
.0313	...	67	.136	....	29	.277	....	J
.032	1/32		.1405	....	28	.281	....	K
.033	...	66	.1406	9/64		.2812	9/32	
.035	...	65	.144	....	27	.290	....	L
.036	...	64	.147	....	26	.295	....	M
.037	...	63	.1495	....	25	.2968	19/64	
.038	...	62	.152	....	24	.302	....	N
.039	...	61	.154	....	23	.3125	5/16	
.040	...	60	.1562	5/32		.316	....	O
.041	...	59	.157	....	22	.323	....	P
.042	...	58	.159	....	21	.3281	21/64	
.043	...	57	.161	....	20	.332	....	Q
.0465	...	56	.166	....	19	.339	....	R
.0468	3/64		.1695	....	18	.3437	11/32	
.052	...	55	.1718	11/64		.348	....	S
.055	...	54	.173	....	17	.358	....	T
.0595	...	53	.177	....	16	.3594	23/64	
.0625	1/16		.180	....	15	.368	....	U
.0635	...	52	.182	....	14	.375	3/8	
.067	...	51	.185	....	13	.377	....	V
.070	...	50	.1875	3/16		.386	....	W
.073	...	49	.189	....	12	.3906	25/64	
.076	...	48	.191	....	11	.397	....	X
.0781	5/64		.1935	....	10	.404	....	Y
.0785	...	47	.196	....	9	.4062	13/32	
.081	...	46	.199	....	8	.413	....	Z
.082	...	45	.201	....	7	.4218	27/64	
.086	...	44	.2031	13/64		.4375	7/16	
.089	...	43	.204	....	6	.4531	29/64	
.0935	...	42	.2055	....	5	.4687	15/32	
.0937	3/32		.209	....	4	.4843	31/64	
			.213	....	3	.500	1/2	

TYPICAL* MECHANICAL PROPERTIES OF WROUGHT ALUMINUM ALLOYS

Alloy and temper	Tension				Hardness	Shear	Fatigue
	Yield strength (set = 0.2%), psi	Ultimate strength, psi	Elongation, per cent in 2 in.		Brinell, 500-kg. load 10-mm. ball	Shearing strength, psi	Endurance limit, psi
			Sheet specimen ($\frac{1}{16}$ in. thick)	Round specimen ($\frac{1}{2}$ in. dia.)			
1100-0	5,000	13,000	35	45	23	9,500	5,000
1100-H12	13,000	15,000	12	25	28	10,000	6,000
1100-H14	14,000	17,000	9	20	32	11,000	7,000
1100-H16	17,000	20,000	6	17	38	12,000	8,500
1100-H18	21,000	24,000	5	15	44	13,000	8,500
3003-0	6,000	16,000	30	40	28	11,000	7,000
3003-H12	15,000	18,000	10	20	35	12,000	8,000
3003-H14	18,000	21,000	8	16	40	14,000	9,000
3003-H16	21,000	25,000	5	14	47	15,000	9,500
3003-H18	25,000	29,000	4	10	55	16,000	.0,000
2017-0	10,000	26,000	20	22	45	18,000	11,000
2017-T4	40,000	62,000	20	22	100	36,000	15,000
Alclad 2017-T4	33,000	56,000	18	..	...	32,000	
2117-T4	24,000	43,000	..	27	70	26,000	13,500
2024-0	10,000	26,000	20	22	42	18,000	12,000
2024-T4	45,000	68,000	19	22	105	41,000	18,000
2024-T36	55,000	70,000	13	..	116	42,000	
Alclad 2024-T	41,000	62,000	18	..	...	40,000	
Alclad 2024-T36	50,000	66,000	11	..	...	41,000	
5052-0	14,000	29,000	25	30	45	18,000	17,000
5052-H12	26,000	34,000	12	18	62	20,000	18,000
5052-H14	29,000	37,000	10	14	67	21,000	19,000
5052-H16	34,000	39,000	8	10	74	23,000	20,000
5052-H18	36,000	41,000	7	8	85	24,000	20,500
6053-0	7,000	16,000	25	35	26	11,000	7,500
6053-T4	20,000	33,000	22	30	65	20,000	10,000
6053-T6	33,000	39,000	14	20	80	24,000	11,000
6061-0	8,000	18,000	22	..	30	12,500	8,000
6061-T4	21,000	35,000	22	..	65	24,000	12,500
6061-T6	39,000	45,000	12	..	95	30,000	12,500
7075-0	15,000	33,000	17	16	60	22,000	
7075-T6	72,000	82,000	11	11	130	49,000	
Alclad 7075-0	14,000	32,000	17	–	–	22,000	
7075-T6	67,000	76,000	11	–	–	46,000	

* These values are *not* guaranteed.

Copyrighted and furnished by courtesy of Aluminum Company of America.

American or Brown & Sharpe for Aluminum & Brass Sheet	Gauge	U.S. Standard Gauge for Steel & Plate Iron & Steel
.3648	00	.3437
.3249	0	.3125
.2893	1	.2812
.2576	2	.2656
.2294	3	.2391
.2043	4	.2242
.1819	5	.2092
.1620	6	.1943
.1443	7	.1793
.1285	8	.1644
.1144	9	.1495
.1019	10	.1345
.0907	11	.1196
.0808	12	.1046
.0720	13	.0897
.0641	14	.0747
.0571	15	.0673
.0508	16	.0598
.0453	17	.0538
.0403	18	.0478
.0359	19	.0418
.0320	20	.0359
.0285	21	.0329
.0253	22	.0299
.0226	23	.0269
.0201	24	.0239
.0179	25	.0209
.0159	26	.0179

Index

Notes

Notes _____

_____

_____

_____

_____

_____

_____

_____

_____

_____

_____

_____

_____

_____

_____

DECIMAL EQUIVALENTS
OF PARTS OF AN INCH

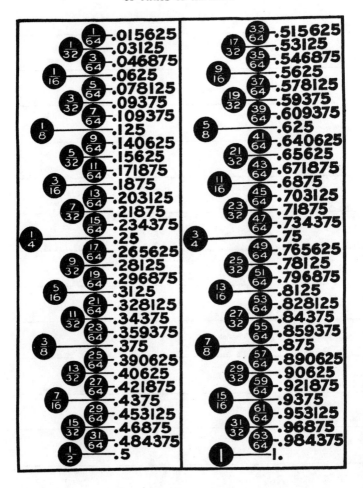

Fraction	Decimal
1/64	.015625
1/32	.03125
3/64	.046875
1/16	.0625
5/64	.078125
3/32	.09375
7/64	.109375
1/8	.125
9/64	.140625
5/32	.15625
11/64	.171875
3/16	.1875
13/64	.203125
7/32	.21875
15/64	.234375
1/4	.25
17/64	.265625
9/32	.28125
19/64	.296875
5/16	.3125
21/64	.328125
11/32	.34375
23/64	.359375
3/8	.375
25/64	.390625
13/32	.40625
27/64	.421875
7/16	.4375
29/64	.453125
15/32	.46875
31/64	.484375
1/2	.5
33/64	.515625
17/32	.53125
35/64	.546875
9/16	.5625
37/64	.578125
19/32	.59375
39/64	.609375
5/8	.625
41/64	.640625
21/32	.65625
43/64	.671875
11/16	.6875
45/64	.703125
23/32	.71875
47/64	.734375
3/4	.75
49/64	.765625
25/32	.78125
51/64	.796875
13/16	.8125
53/64	.828125
27/32	.84375
55/64	.859375
7/8	.875
57/64	.890625
29/32	.90625
59/64	.921875
15/16	.9375
61/64	.953125
31/32	.96875
63/64	.984375
1	1.